A TALE
OF
TWO DOCTORS

A TALE
OF
TWO DOCTORS

by

DR. SABINA SKOPIŃSKA

(Translated from Polish by Magda Czajkowska)

and

DR. MONIKA BLACKWELL

Foreword by Dr. Stefan Cembrowicz

Clinical Press Ltd.
Bristol UK

A catalogue record for this book is available from the British Library

ISBN 978-1-85-457104-5
A tale of two doctors: Monika Blackwell

Cover design: Paul R Goddard. Old Stethoscope, Alan Peck Medical Archives, saved by Dr Kedra Fairley

Published in 2021 by:
Clinical Press Ltd.
Redland Green Farm, Redland, Bristol, BS6 7HF

CONTENTS

Page number

Foreword: Stefan Cembrowicz ... 7
Introduction ... 9
Photograph: Dr Sabina Skopinska ... 12
A Doctor's Diary: Dr Sabina Skopinska ... 13
Introduction ... 13
My Poznan Practice ... 15
Photograph: The town of S. (Starołęka) ... 15
A doctor's living quarters ... 18
Local inhabitants and the new doctor ... 18
Free choice of a doctor ... 21
Night visits of a country doctor ... 23
Living conditions of workers and labourers in the district ... 24
Transport ... 26
Medical Practice in Villages ... 27
Village Poverty ... 28
Easter ... 30
And now for the horror ... 31
Emergency Cases ... 32
Alcoholism in the country ... 35
Births, miscarriages, illegitimate children ... 36
A cry in the night ... 39
Infectious Diseases ... 39
A throat abscess ... 40
The "rash" ... 41
The 1929 Influenza epidemic ... 42
Malingering ... 43
Tuberculosis ... 46
Work in the brickyard and in the artificial fertiliser factory ... 51
About the young generation and amelioration of the rural districts ... 52
Unemployment ... 54
The Amusement Park ... 56
The first generation of the worker intelligentsia ... 58
An economics exam ... 59
Something's not quite right ... 60

Contents: continued

Attempts at blackmail	61
The Poznań children	63
The doctor and the bailiff	64
Photograph: A Polish village in the 1920s	67
My Warsaw Practice	67
My patients	68
A tender, sensitive nature	69
Liver disease	71
Syphilis	72
A Lady with influence	74
A secretary to the minister	76
Two men with duodenal ulcer	77
The only cure for a painful toe is to cut the leg off	78
"Seriously ill"	79
Cancer	81
Some socio-literary reflections and about five drinkers	86
Social Insurance – an object of dislike	90
Profession – actress	94
The Ministry of Foreign Affairs	97
Confidence Gained	98
A grateful old lady	101
Marital Confidences	104
It's not a bed of roses	107
About cobblers, print-setters and TB in Warsaw	108
Comments	109
Photograph: Warsaw before the Second World War	112
Photograph: Warsaw – Łazienki Park	113
Photograph: Memorial to Sabina	113
Dr Monika Blackwell: A second Doctor's Diary	114
Acknowledgments	131
Photograph: Dr Monika Blackwell	131

Foreword

Dr Sabina Skopińska, the remarkable grandmother of Dr Monika Blackwell, worked in the same prewar world in which my own father practiced (until arrested in 1939 by the NKVD).

Her holistic values shine down the years to GPs even now, as she struggled singlehandedly to operate the Byzantine complexities of Poland's newly reborn health system, dealt with all comers at all hours as well as with her own exhaustion, bereavement and money worries, and struggled to make her rigidly technical training fit every shade of human existence.

Without the support of any young principals' group, mentor, peers or senior partner to tell her how to deal with sick notes, red tape, and human nature, she tackled her at times garrulous patients head on, with all their deprivation, superstition, fickleness, bravery, ignorance - and charm. Sounds familiar?

She didn't choose an easy furrow to plough. There were other ways for wellborn young doctors from her *szlachta* (landed gentry) background to earn a comfortable living. Her training, entirely theoretical and physical, must have left her completely unprepared for the social and psychological problems she was to encounter.

Though her world, with its idyllic, pastoral riverscapes and reeking rural slums, seems so far from our twenty first century one, the TB and rickets she was so familiar with are not extinct in today's UK. Families in poverty, homelessness and with chronic alcohol problems remain with us the world over. Poverty, disease, ignorance, squalor and idleness were yet to be defined by Beveridge as the targets of Britain's future Welfare State. And Dr Skopińska encountered all of these full-on.

She was drawn towards the left of Poland's wide political spectrum, and forty years before the UK's Black Report she was clearly aware of the inverse care law - where the poorest are the illest.

She became an activist, practiced social medicine, and faced the overwhelming problems she encountered with a steadfast and uncompromising spirit.

But my father survived, and she perished. In 1943, five years after she wrote this diary, she was to die in Warsaw, in a shootout with the Gestapo at her clandestine underground radio station. The clarity of her values shines on - and it's good to know that such genes are not extinct.

Stefan Cembrowicz
March 2021

Introduction

Dr.Sabina Skopińska 25.10.1900 – 14.09.1943

Biography

Born in Warsaw, at that time part of the Russian empire, Sabina began her studies in St.Petersburg (subsequently named Leningrad). Once Poland regained independence after WW1 she returned home to continue and finish her studies at the Warsaw Medical School.

In 1925 she moved to Poznań and settled in Starołęka which was on the outskirts. Working as a GP for the Social Insurance and Healthcare Fund, she looked after peasants, farmers and labourers. Moved by their poverty and low standard of living she also became involved in social work. She was chairwoman of the Working Women's Organisation, Councillor in the Poznań city council, was involved in the Scouting movement and in the Polish Red Cross.

In 1935 she moved back to Warsaw where she looked after mainly lower echelons of society. She described her work there and in Poznań in her "Diary".

The "Diary" was written in 1938 in response to a national competition to which doctors working for the Social Insurance and Healthcare Fund were invited to respond. 51 doctors sent in their entries, Sabina received second prize. At the time, Poland's population was 4.9 million people of whom 16% were insured. There were fifteen hospital beds per 10,000 population and 3.7 doctors for this number. (This compares with the UK population in 2019 of 66.6 million people, twenty nine hospital beds per 10,000 population and 28 doctors for this number with near universal health care cover.)

During the German occupation of Poland in WW2 she was involved in the Peasants Freedom Organisation which was then incorporated into the (underground) Resistance – the A.K. (Armia Krajowa – the Home Army). Her apartment became the centre of clandestine meetings of the Warsaw Central Branch of A.K. and of the Government Delegation. Thanks to her perfect Russian she used to monitor then translate beamed messages from the Soviet Union(it was forbidden to own a radio) and pass them on to the A.K. command. She also ran a clandestine training course for nurses there. Such training, together with all aspects of higher education, was forbidden to Poles by the occupying German forces.

In 1943 she was shot dead in her apartment by the Gestapo during a monitoring session.

Sabina was married twice. Her first husband Włodzimierz Dębczyński, father of her only child Zbigniew, was an army doctor serving in the 14th Light Field Artillery, who died in 1929 in a car accident. Her second marriage to Prof. Dr. Stefan Różycki ended in divorce.

For her wartime work Sabina was posthumously awarded the Cross of Valour and the Gold Cross of Merit with Swords. A commemorative plaque erected in the Church of St. Teresa in Warsaw was unveiled in November 1979.

Sabina's son Zbigniew spoke little about his beloved mother. He mentioned one incident which never failed to bring a smile. During the war one of Sabina's patients was a German soldier from the Wehrmacht. To thank her for successful treatment he brought a gift – a live goose, a most welcome gift in those days of severe food shortages. While he was sitting in the waiting room holding the goose, another patient came in, a lady with a bulldog. On seeing the goose the bulldog attacked. The terrified goose broke away from the soldier's hands squawking and flying all over the room chased by the dog. Feathers flying, dog barking, the pandemonium that ensued was not without danger. There was nothing to stop the soldier taking out his pistol and shooting the lot; the Germans during the Occupation were quite capable of it.

The other memory was of the beginning of the war. After the bombardment of Warsaw there was no food to be had at all. Mother and son were left with only a few eggs and some dry bread in their pantry and little prospect of buying anything else. It was divided between them as follows – their cat was given the precious eggs, mother and son had the dry bread.

As to what happened during that fatal monitoring is subject to conjecture through lack of witnesses. We do know that Sabina was not alone; there was a man with her also from the Resistance, listening to the broadcasting. His name is unknown, but then members of A.K. only used pseudonyms so as not to divulge the identity of its members if caught and tortured. It is assumed that when the Gestapo broke into the apartment, he pulled a gun and in the ensuing firefight they were shot on the spot. Both his body and Sabina, dead or dying, were taken to the Gestapo headquarters. Her body was released a few days later. She was buried in the family grave in the Powązki cemetery in Warsaw (Grave No. B61, alley 299) next to her brother-in-law murdered earlier in a concentration camp. Only her nearest family were present as the funeral was monitored by the Gestapo and Zbigniew could only watch it from afar.

Zbigniew, also in the Resistance, but in a different unit, managed to escape, pushed out through the back door of the apartment by his mother while the Gestapo was breaking down the front door, and ran up to the attic. The Gestapo proceeded to search the whole building. When he heard footsteps going up the stairs he jumped from an open window across the roof and swung himself into the attic of the neighbouring block of flats.

He was given a new set of identity papers by the Resistance in order not to connect him to Sabina as she was on the Gestapo wanted list as were all who were associated with her. His new name and identity was *"Czajkowski, born in Warsaw"* which he used for the rest of his life. He went on to fight in the Warsaw Uprising, which he described in his *"Diary of the Insurgent"* initially in the form of letters to his grandmother, to tell her about his activities there. After the Warsaw capitulation he was taken prisoner to a PoW camp in Germany. When the war ended he went to a Polish school in Lubeck, passed his *matura* (school leavers certificate) and came to England. He went on to study engineering in London and obtained an M.Sc. degree. He settled in England and made it his home marrying Magdalena Zaziemska in 1956. They had two children, both doctors – Monika Blackwell and Marek Czajkowski. He died of leukaemia in 1999.

Translator's Notes

S. or the town of S. = Starołęka – town within the district of the city of Poznań, now its suburb
Healthcare Fund = Kasa Chorych
Council Healthcare Fund = Powiatowa Kasa Chorych
Social Insurance = Ubezpieczalnia Społeczna
Value of the złoty = 1 zł in 1930s = 17 zł in 2010s, based on
the published average monthly pay of the two periods

The Healthcare Fund

The Healthcare Fund was founded in 1921. It was a self-governing body providing health care for the qualified, that is the employed. To belong to it was compulsory, limited to the area in which the employed lived. It gave full medical care to an employed person, his family, hospitalisation, obstetrics, funeral expenses, supply of medicines and the issue of sickness certificates. Medical care was carried out by GPs. Contributions were paid partly by the employer and partly by the employee. The insured was issued with a membership card in which were listed the medical services carried out and payments of the subscription fees.

In 1933 the "Healthcare Fund" was incorporated into the "Social Insurance".

✳✳✳✳

Dr Sabina Skopinska

Dr Sabina Skopinska

Introduction

I am a doctor who carried out about one hundred thousand patient consultations. Twelve years of my life were devoted to the Social Health Services, and now I would like to sum up the results of my work.

The law of life which invests with gravity everything in the world, and death, that pitiless death with which doctors continue to fight, influenced all that I managed to achieve. This diary is but a weak reflection of this continuous, fierce battle, the battle in which not only the sick suffer but also those who come to their aid. These are not empty words of a doctor fighting for the life of her patients because when they cannot be helped it affects the doctor too. That is why there is little joy in this Diary.

Time and place: Warsaw, long ago. I am sitting in the top row of the lecture theatre hall of the Infant Jesus Hospital. Down below our lecturer Professor G. is standing between the desk and the patient's bed. While he examines the patient we, the students, watch in silence. He marks the periphery of the enlarged heart muscle by tapping the chest with his fingers. The examination is delicate and precise, the change in the sound of tapping can be heard even where I am sitting.

Professor G. continues to examine the patient gently. Unfortunately in all his organs he finds pathological changes. He writes their Latin names on the blackboard. He finds the kidney and the heart infected. In the circumstances all other organs cannot remain healthy. We, the students write down around 15 Latin names of the diseases found as the result of the examination before the patient is wheeled away. His condition is hopeless. Professor G. ends the lecture with the words:

"In a few days' time we will be able to verify the diagnosis based on today's examination with what we shall find after the autopsy of the corpse."

In that moment I stopped being a young medical student. I was overcome by an uneasy feeling, like the time when I first went into the dissection room. So, the body of this person I saw alive today will in a few days' time be lying in front of us, cut up, so that we'll be able to check whether the diagnosis arrived at was correct.

Just so. Medicine is truly an experimental science.

*

I worked diligently in Professor G's clinic. I was proud to be a junior doctor in the first clinic of the University of Warsaw. Something was telling me what I will learn there will be my professional investment for the rest of my life, to which I'll be able to add only from time to time. That's exactly what happened. Having finished my studies and the compulsory hospital practice I left for Poznań. Unable to find employment in Warsaw, prompted by the need to earn my living I accepted a post of a junior doctor at the university of Poznań in the department of descriptive anatomy, as well as taking practical classes of students in the dissecting room and organising a series of lectures on physical education. This greatly added to my knowledge of theoretical medicine, but I was ill at ease with its academic side, preferring practical medicine to collecting material for academic articles. Apart from that, St. Bureaucrat leaves no one in peace in Poland. A junior doctor working at a university also had to deal with administration. I did it very reluctantly. It distressed me having to listen to my boss's complaints that the accounts of the scientific donations every university had to account for were not properly set out, that my writing was undecipherable, and so on. I also had to look after the stores of teaching materials, microscopes, instruments as well as inventories and catalogues of books. Added to that were the animals - dogs and guinea pigs kept for vivisections for scientific research.

In those two years I was able to meet a considerable number of candidates for future doctors. Most of them, including myself, found the non-clinical medicine, which at the time was disproportionately emphasised, not popular, as opposed to the much preferred clinical medicine. For three years a student had to study all possible ins and outs of descriptive, topographic medicine, histology, chemistry and physics. For three years he/she never saw a sick person. In 1926 the Poznań university had no clinics of its own and had to depend on the military and city hospitals.

I thanked the fates which allowed me to study at the Warsaw University where in spite of a great number of students, it was possible to attend the clinics. Professors of Clinical medicine were equally demanding as the theoretical ones. For example, in order to pass an exam in pathological anatomy under professor H. (deceased) one had to "swot" for at least 6 months, alongside other subjects demanding the same amount of time in order to prepare oneself for the finals.

In Poznań the teaching of the theory was greatly disproportionate to the practice. Poland at that time struggled to maintain five universities and the University of Poznań in particular had its own organisational problems. I also observed the marked enthusiasm to attain the material benefits that resulted from obtaining a medical degree among even quite young doctors. Of course, everyone wants to have a career and to earn money but the speed with which some seemed to embrace this made me feel quite dizzy.

My Poznan Practice

While working as an assistant at the university I had a fair amount of free time. I used it to broaden my practical medicine studies and also to be registered by the Medical Union in order to join the Healthcare Fund of the district of Poznań. The year was 1925. Apart from having the necessary qualifications, a doctor applying for registration was required to "live in" the area. That meant having one's own consulting facilities in order to see patients at set times.

The town of S. (Starołęka)

15

The insured had a free choice of a doctor. The insured person would go to the Healthcare Fund, and take his card to one of the 120 doctors who were registered in the Healthcare Fund in the administrative district of Poznań. When I was practising, was wholly dependent on the Medical Union. At that time the registration was granted reluctantly, because there were too many doctors practising in the city but not enough in the suburbs. One example was in the town of S. situated 7 km from the centre of Poznań where there were a number of large factories making steam tractors and locomotives, artificial fertilisers and several smaller ones and workshops. There was not a single doctor for the 3000 registered insured.

Communication from the city Poznań in 1925 was not easy. One travelled by train or a horse-drawn cart for 7 km., or alternatively had to walk 3 km. to a tram stop across a railway bridge and follow narrow paths through a lovely park by the river Varta. I went to see S. and found it charming, situated by the river Varta which was very picturesque. Spanning the river was a railway bridge with tiny towers which looked like a small medieval castle. There was a power mill and big, brick 4-storey silos standing by the river, also decorated by tiny towers, all of them contributing to an overall charm of the town. The mill which ran non-stop was particularly beautiful, its electric lights reflecting mysteriously at night in the fast flowing river, while the rhythmic beat of its machinery echoed in the oak woods and groves on the opposite side. I have to thank this almost theatrical setting which to a large extent had influenced my decision to settle in S.

Lack of communication had a major effect on the local population. It must be stressed the inhabitants were not completely deprived of healthcare. Dr. X had a practice in the city. He came to S. twice a week to see patients for two hours in a rented room. Insured patients would queue on the stairs while waiting for him to arrive. While at the same time practising as an Army doctor, he would arrive after 6 pm in order to deal with the patients waiting for him after finishing his clinics in Poznan. The Healthcare Fund was very dissatisfied with this state of affairs, as were the inhabitants. In cases of emergency there was absolutely no doctor who could be called for help. There was no emergency ambulance service. Only 5-6 trains ran between Poznań and S. so no doctor could arrive from Poznań and return quickly, nor could a patient go to a doctor without wasting at least five hours due to inconvenient train time tables. And taxi fares were very expensive.

The health care in 1925 in S. worked like this. Dr X came 2-3 times a week for two hours in the evening. Apart from Dr X, a graduate medical student from Odessa, a lieutenant orderly, also practiced in the town for 2 hours in the evening 2-3 times a week and enjoyed free accommodation. He dealt privately with those whom Dr X had ran out of time to see. Apart from those two, there was a traditional healer (known as a *"wise woman"*) who applied herbs, magic and incantations. She lived in the Colony, a settlement built by railway workers. She had a considerable following, and continued to treat the inhabitants of S. up to 1930 in this, after all, enlightened country. I should add, her sons were later my patients. In this way the above assembled team treated the three thousand insured and their families.

There was a tiny pharmacy in S. The owner, a very pleasant man, an entrepreneurial type, urged me to settle down here. The Poznań Healthcare Fund had its own pharmacy in the city but it did not set one up in S. and the insured would have to walk 7km. for a prescription. The pharmacist managed to negotiate a franchise for a pharmacy and was keen to have a resident local doctor. He was very helpful, and even suggested I could live in the house where he had his pharmacy. The owner of the house was a baker, a Polonised German since his grandfather's days, who was willing to sell his apartment together with the furniture. At the time property could also be rented in the town of S. As I mentioned, in order to receive the right to practice for the Healthcare Fund, apart from medical qualifications, had to have considerable capital in order to buy an apartment and set up the consulting and waiting rooms. Doctors who were General (or Family) practitioners had to have a cabinet with instruments, a couch for gynaecological examinations and a wash basin in every consulting room. One had to save and scrimp in order to buy all those things. But my dislike for medical administration was too great, and the wish for direct contact with life so attractive that setting aside all the difficulties, I decided to settle down in S.

A doctor's living quarters

After deciding to move to S. I had encountered many unpleasant difficulties, mainly in finding a place to live. The apartment I found was in an outbuilding. The house itself stood on a hill just above the river in, for me, an enchanting place, between the railway bridge and that mill emitting those rhythmic sounds. The windows looked out on the oak wood and lovely groves stretching along the opposite side of the river Varta. But all that was poetry. The prosaic reality however was as follows – no indoor plumbing or toilet facilities, no electricity only gas lighting. The entrance was through a yard containing pigs and chickens, there was no telephone, no communication with the city, not to mention the considerable monetary deposit and the monthly rent.

Local inhabitants and the new doctor

Apart from the financial aspects of settling in the town of S. in 1922, there were personal challenges which gave me cause for reflection. When I first arrived the local inhabitants' reaction was hostile, not because I was a very young woman doctor. That didn't matter much. My female colleagues had a good reputation and people liked to see women doctors. No, the reason they disliked me was that I wasn't *'from here'*, I wasn't local, not one of them. I arrived from a different part of Poland, in their imagination of warmth and sunshine, and came here to snatch bread from the locals' mouths. That was the general opinion.

I managed to discover the following intriguing plot. A fellow tenant, the wife of a labourer in one of the local factories, was going round the houses collecting signatures in a campaign against me as the non-local doctor. She supported Dr X, who only came to the clinic twice a week. I discovered her campaign which I am sure was spontaneous and not supported by him. In fact she managed to advertise me. Because of her, people found out that in this town there was now a local doctor who could be called upon in an emergency. And this is what happened. Night visits, and seeing patients in the early mornings instantly became my domain. However, as far as the afternoons were concerned patients were divided. Most would continue to see Dr. X. After my arrival he still practised for over a year, even though he was not allowed to run two private clinics. Obviously my earnings at that time were small because the "Fund" patients were getting used to the new doctor very slowly. Also, my reputation among the peasant and labourer families was that I was too innovative, because I told them to take their clothes off for an examination. The patients were not used to that. What they were used to was waiting on the stairs, receiving medicines depending on what they looked like or symptom-based as long as they tasted alright. They had to get used to my new ways of examining them and being prescribed medicines that sometimes didn't taste very nice.

The favourite occupation of this parochial suburb of Poznań was to watch the goings on outside on the street through the window, lying on cushions, a habit, I believe, shared by most small, provincial towns. Some people even had special little mirrors fixed at an angle which allowed them to see both sides of the road at any one time. My housekeeper, a stout baker's wife, observing me for a month while I ran from one sick person to another said:

'You are moving too fast for me, I can't catch up with you. I only need to turn my head and you are already on the other end of the road.'

Nothing of my external appearance could appeal to the portly ladies of S. not my body size, no celebratory air of gravitas expected of the medical profession, no material wealth. Living in a baker's outbuilding while all the prominent citizens lived in their own little houses did not add to my prestige. To top it all my clear, accent-less Polish among people who spoke the dialect, and a very specific dialect at that, also added to the general air of otherness. The dialect of the inhabitants was not without charm. Many words were derived from the German but many also from old Polish.[1] There were not many of the younger generations in the town who attended Polish schools. The inhabitants remembered the Germans well and not only the oldest generation. Most of those who could read and write in Polish attended clandestine classes before and during the war, and it was those who spoke the dialect.

At first, when a patient spoke to me in the dialect telling me he has a persistent cough I was not sure what he was talking about. But

Note 1: Before regaining independence in 1918 Poland was divided between her neighbours. Poznań was part of Germany.

19

in time I managed to learn some of the words and used them when examining patients. The local pharmacist was a great help, explaining and translating the words and the names of their medicines .

People were accustomed to cure themselves with their own favourite folk remedies. They would ask me to prescribe them *"The Drops of St.Jack"* or *"The Drops of St.Genevieve"*, and great quantities of ointments they could rub in. There was practically no patient suffering from a *"stitch"* or *"colic"* (their words) who believed oral medication was any good. Stitch and colic could only be relieved by an ointment. I had to step in very slowly into that mire of folk superstition and beliefs. I learned my lesson from the piles of broken bottles outside the local pharmacy. I had to reach out to my patients, had to gain their trust at all cost. And so I listened to whatever patients told me, even though it was downright stupid and superstitious. Nevertheless I was not prepared to prescribe what they dictated, such as the *"Tincture of 9 "* or the *"Green Ointment"* for wounds. None of the names they asked for figured in what I had been taught at the university. The local pharmacist told me that the *"Tincture of 9"* contained valerian dissolved in ether and that medicines were only acceptable if they contained ether. This worked very well and I was able to prescribe a whole range of medications for the heart, alimentary canal or nervous system because they reassuringly smelled of ether.

However, it was worse with the *"rubbing"* ointments. What was there to rub into the skin when the *"colic"* was caused by a gall bladder infection, or kidney, or stomach, when the patient stated categorically they only believed in *"rubbing"* and would not take any medication orally. Some patients would never take anything in powder form, firmly convinced that powder is poisonous, never for a moment suspecting that they were taking that medication in the form of liquids or in drops.

Injections were worst of all. As far as they were concerned every injection shortened a life by a year. I was once called to a sick woman suffering from stomach cancer. She twisted and turned in unimaginable agony. I gave her an injection of morphine and another for the heart. She died two days later and, of course, everybody believed her death was caused by those injections.

I decided at all cost not to give in to this opposition to new, curative methods. The local pharmacist gave me a herbal formulary with local names of herbs and their medical uses which I compared with their Latin names, and somehow managed to steer a course amidst the constant dangers threatening a doctor's profession.

Free choice of a doctor

Until 1934 in the district of Poznań the insured could choose their own doctor for each consultation. Hence I had no steady income for treating the insured and their families. What I earned was solely dependent on how many patients came to see me. For a consultation in a doctor's surgery I was paid a fee set by the Healthcare Fund working in conjunction with the Medical Union. For a doctor's day visit the set fee was tripled, for a night visit multiplied by nine.

This system would have been ideal if some of the insured did not abuse it, often going with non-existing ailments to several of the one hundred and twenty doctors registered in Poznań, or if there were not a great number of malingerers who were out to obtain sickness benefits for non-existing ailments. Personally, I never came across a patient with a threatening look coming to my surgery for a sickness certificate, or an employer who 'pays hence demands' which I frequently encountered later in Warsaw.

But this freedom of choice could not be borne by any insurance company. There were situations where a patient would present his card to a different doctor every week in order to find out which medicine tasted better or was more effective. Outside the pharmacy in S. I often saw a heap of broken medicine bottles. A 'sick' person having tasted the medicine on leaving the pharmacy and not liking the taste would either break the whole bottle, or pour out the contents and keep the bottle. He would then go to another doctor and repeat the process. I have also heard from the pharmacist that patients would trade their medications. I think if they had had to pay for a doctor's consultation and prescriptions directly they would have had more respect for what they have been given by the Social Insurance. A new rule brought in 1934 had acknowledged the situation and brought in small contributions from the patients.

21

I did not belong to the so-called *"top scorers"*, meaning I did not manage to reach the top score of one thousand and eight hundred points set by the Healthcare Fund. I will explain. Poznań doctors did not have a regular, steady income but were paid singly for every consultation and separately for every treatment. A consultation earned one point which was paid in several ways. The Council Healthcare Fund paid on the average one zloty.[2] For an agricultural worker the Council Healthcare Fund paid half of that. For every kilometre of travel to visit a patient it was double (there and back), for an intramuscular injection the same, for an intravenous injection: three points. In other words, every possible treatment carried out by a doctor was converted into points.

An optician received payment in points for an eye examination, not only for the consultation itself, but would add the number of points he expected to have to carry out during that consultation when applying to the Healthcare Fund.

As happens in every walk of life, there was a spectrum of doctors in the Medical Union. There were those who scored a great number of points by sparing a patient nothing and over-investigating. At a meeting of the Medical Union it was even said that at the time when an anal examination gained one point, there were doctors who would investigate every other patient in this way, admirably doubling their salary.

Thus huge sums were initially paid out by the City Healthcare Fund in the years 1924-25. The Medical Union Board finally intervened and set a top score of 1800 points per month, justifying their decision by the fact a doctor could not possibly deal with more than 60 patients in a day. I say 'deal with' because to carry out an honest, thorough investigation in such a short time, especially as the free choice of a doctor could facilitate unnecessary follow up attendances purely with the aim of increasing an unscrupulous doctor's salary.

In spite of this limit there were *"Fund sharks"*, as their colleagues called them, who managed to score 2000 points. Those extra points were disallowed, a fact they greatly resented, while the Medical Union energetically fought this kind of behaviour. I was once present at a

Note 2. 1 zl. equiv. to 17 zl. in 2010, today's value.£3.50 – figures approximate

meeting during which the *"Top Scorers"* and *"Sharks"* were reprimanded by reading out aloud the prescriptions they issued. I heard the names I knew well – the *'Ear Drops'*, the *'Tincture of 9'*, the *'Tincture of 3'* the *'Ointment of St. Anne'* and so on.

At the time I was determined not to go with the flow, and not give up. If I had acquiesced, I would probably have acquired a huge practice, and my prescriptions might have been read out publicly as a curiosity. But, there is a reverse side to this coin. I could not afford to buy somewhere to live, not even a tiny house in S. Of course, I don't regret it, but can understand the temptations which beset young, inexperienced doctors working for the Healthcare Fund.

Night visits of a country doctor

Getting up in the middle of the night to see a sick person was one of the hardest duties of a doctor, particularly as a full day's work awaited the following morning.

Before I got used to it, the first moments of getting out of bed were the hardest. Once outside, and if it was Spring or autumn, and was not raining too hard, it could become quite pleasant. Often the moon and stars lit the way making up for the total lack of electric street lighting. The river was even lovelier than during the day, and the ripple of the streams flowing into it made an enchanting sound. I think a person appreciative of the beauty of nature is at least twice as well off to the one who is indifferent to the deep blue sky or not moved on seeing the stars.

The extremely hard work involving those night visits, filled as I was with anxiety (would I manage, would I be able to make the correct diagnosis, will I be able to help that sick person?) was compensated for by this trip and the return journey. It made the horrors which I had witnessed easier to bear.

The air in the sickrooms was often heavy and smelly. Sometimes I encountered terrible scenes and witnessed my patients' appalling living conditions. All this affected me deeply. Yet, after leaving the sick, once outside, I would take a deep breath of fresh air, and my strength would return to deal with more difficulties and witness more evidence of the dreadful living conditions of our village people.

Living conditions of workers and labourers in the district

Within a one and a half to two kilometre radius of S. are scattered villages where live what I would describe as agro-workers, that is people employed both in agriculture and in factories. At the times when the factories were open they would work there, when they closed, they worked on the land. The two biggest factories employing hundreds of people took on people according to orders received. The same system applied to the numerous smaller factories and workshops. Thus the number of insured patients fluctuated accordingly. This was the time of relative economic prosperity and on the whole people were reasonably well off.

I had the opportunity to observe these people and admire their desire to own a piece of land. An average labourer would send his son to work in a factory as soon as he grew up, and as soon as he could he would buy a tiny piece of land to build on, getting building materials from goodness only knows where, and doing all the jobs himself. One of my female patients told me while I changed a dressing on her leg, that both she and her husband painted their tiny one-room cottage using a mixture of brine and a laundry dye. Maybe that's how it's done, I know nothing about such things, but I was struck by how resourceful people were. What a difference between them and the Warsaw workers I was to meet later. I mention this because I want to describe the living conditions of these agro-workers I looked after for seven years.

The housing conditions in the district were often abysmal. This, of course, did not apply to everyone. There were those who had already built their houses and lived two or three in one room. But this was rather rare. At this time, lack of housing in the suburbs was critical. Immigrants arriving from Germany and France who had been evicted from Poznan, had settled in and around the town of S. as tenants and sub-tenants in designated houses. But not only there. In the town of S. there were old fortifications built by the Germans, known as the 'Forts' which people squatted in. The Fort 'A', to give an example, was a brick building rising 2-3 metres above the ground level, the roof covered by soil, on which grew grass and fair-sized bushes as well. A number of tenants evicted from Poznan lived in that 'Fort'.

On my visits to the sick I had to climb down cranky stairs and walk along dark, damp corridors permeated by fusty smell, with water running down the walls. My patients lived in large rooms divided into three using wooden boards, paper and rags. The only light came from a single, tiny window. Water ran down the walls so that wardrobes and beds had to stand away from them. They were soaking wet because of water dripping from the ceiling.

I looked after at least fifty patients living in those conditions.

Many others did not come to see me, so I am not sure how many people in total lived in the 'Forts'. Let me politely ask you how in those circumstances was I to treat such ailments as rheumatism of the joints, TB, breathing problems caused by heart conditions or asthma?

This is where the benefits of the Social Insurance came fully to the fore. I was able to send the seriously sick living in those conditions to hospitals and sanatoria. In less serious cases, if they were chronic as in rheumatism, or intermittent such as asthma, and the patient could not stop working, then I had to do what I could in the circumstances. My biggest nightmare was asthma attacks. Dampness, mould growing in damp places, hair of various animals such as cats, would bring on an attack. The bronchi tighten up, the patient cannot breathe and suffocates. The doctor could help fairly quickly by applying medication, usually by injection. As there were no emergency facilities in the district, and I was the only resident doctor, I had to run at breakneck speed, be it day or night, to inject a patient.

One unpleasant incident stays with me to this day. I was called to 'The Forts' to visit an old couple. I knocked and opened the door. Without any warning or no sound a big, black dog pounced on me and bit me tearing my clothes. The old couple were senile, the man suffered from asthma and arteriosclerosis, the woman from dementia, and did not notice what had happened. Luckily I always take my doctor's case with me and was able to put on a dressing intended for patients on my leg. It was almost impossible to find out if the dog was a carrier of rabies, and the possibilities of further complications worried me for a long time. The wound festered for a long time. I carry the 'souvenir' of that incident in the form of a peeling scar to this day..

Transport

When I first opened my practice I had no means of transport. I would walk to villages lying within a three kilometres radius, but if they lived five kilometres or more a horse-drawn cart would be fetched for me. Be it night, frost, rain or mud I would mount a trap or a cart to visit my patients. People were even surprised at my courage, because at night everything appears intimidating. It wasn't really pleasant when an unwashed and dishevelled farm hand driving a cart filled with straw arrived to fetch me because a woman was haemorrhaging. But nothing bad ever happened to me during those drives, and it would not be me if I didn't enjoy this journey on a moonlit, frosty night, or on a sunny day along the sandy, dusty roads.

In the Poznań district there were few main roads. I travelled to the villages in the district by side roads, shaken in those peasant carts, as the only straight road led just to the nearest town to S. One could only travel to the surrounding villages by the good old Polish beaten dirt tracks, sinking into the mud when it rained or into the sand in a heat wave.

My practice grew from day to day. In the ten years I was there I was called to around twenty-six villages scattered around the Poznań district. After three years I managed to buy a car from my savings and on credit, in order to deal with my patients more quickly. Tragically six months later the car was involved in a terrible accident. It crashed into a roadside tree instantly killing my husband who was driving it. Now I was a widow.

I went to work with doubled energy, having to bring up my three year old son, as well as having to pay back my debts incurred in the purchase of the car. Deprived of means of transport needing to access twenty-six villages, I could not cope without a car but had no resources to buy another. Luckily, the owner of a well-maintained, solid taxi came to my rescue with a 'Chevrolet' which was very suitable for the roads on which I had to travel. Only American cars such as 'Ford' or 'Chevrolet' with their chassis mounted high off the ground could be driven on those roads. All others, even expensive and luxurious ones, sunk into the sand, mud or snow. Others had problems with their cooling systems which froze during the winter months.

With time people in the district came to hear about me while the town of S. slowly modernised. That had a positive effect on my work because I came to know a greater number of patients. Once a bus service was introduced running every half hour between S. and Poznań I could finally send patients to the specialists. Also, emergency services began to function which released me from having to deal with emergency cases myself.

Medical Practice in Villages

[Dr.Sabina lists the names of 24 villages to which she was called out]

Some of those villages I had to visit every other day. Due to the distances between the villages, a day's work by car could cover 60 km. Sometimes reaching these villages cost me more in terms of my own health and nerves than the most serious medical cases I had been called to deal with.

When I drove to a village in late autumn, winter, or early Spring, I had the impression of having arrived at some remote African village. Crowds of children would gather round the car. The driver had to constantly shoo them away while they, with great enthusiasm, tried to unscrew the lamps or the number plates. I must admit the driver was exceptionally resourceful. We had very few breakdowns and even fewer punctures. On arrival at a village he always checked the engine and cleaned the car which at times was so covered in mud one could not even see the windows.

Usually after arrival I had to examine four or five bedridden patients lying in huts reached by almost sinking waist high in mud. At times a boy would volunteer to guide me past potential traps in the form of manure pits covered with straw in front of the dwellings guarded by dogs tied to long chains. There was no certainty whether the chains were sufficiently short to stop the dogs from attacking me. And so I trudged with my guide along endless fences trying to miss the various potholes.

If the room of the bed-ridden was large then after I had seen my patient, a number of insured labourers would come to ask me for prescriptions, such as cod liver oil for the children, dressings for various wounds, eye drops, and those popular ointments for various 'colics'. The room would become a tiny consulting room, the sick would form a queue with one holding a thermometer in his armpit, another would be showing me his throat, the third a sore leg.

At other times I would carry out consultations in the open, as I was getting in to the car. There would be groups of people standing around the car asking for advice and medicines. But then does it matter where the consultations take place, as long as sick people come to see a doctor they trust?

In the summer I would often see patients sitting on a bench outside a hut, rather than in a stifling room inside. There I had a chance to talk to them and prescribe the necessary medicines. Once we got to know each other better my patients were often very grateful and kind, which they expressed this by decorating the car with greenery and flowers tied to the lamps, or thrown inside. I don't think I shall ever receive more flowers in my life than those given to me then by unknown persons. Never did flowers seem more beautiful than those bundles of chamomiles given from a generous heart. Those tokens of gratitude cheered me up enormously; nevertheless I would return home after a journey of tens of kilometres with a sore throat and a painful spine.

At home dinner would have been already cleared away. I would not allow them to wait for me because I was never sure when I would be back. I would throw myself on the bed to rest, look at the flowers and think about the people who gave them to me. Maybe it's those flowers that brought about the reflections which I am now sharing with my readers. They were, after all, tokens of gratitude given by people who were not even aware how poor they were, how unhappy and abandoned, living in villages which, to reach them in autumn or winter, felt almost like an expedition to a virgin jungle.

Village Poverty

I am putting this question to you, rationally and calmly, even though my heart is pounding and I can barely hold pen to paper because words seem inadequate – who knows and who is aware of what is happening to the people living in Polish villages? This question is directed to the intelligent and the educated. Have they any idea of the poverty which exists there, even in the most advanced parts of Poland? There, TB reigns supreme, spreading its wings like a monstrous vampire hovering above the silence of village cemeteries.

I often quoted to myself the words of our poet Wyspiański – *"Ah our villages – tranquil and calm"* when, as a newly arrived young doctor, I tried to discover the hidden mystery of that idyllic rural life. Since that time I cannot remain tranquil and happy, I cannot forget what I have seen.

I am reminded of an incident in the winter of 1931. I arrived at a hut by the roadside, with a half-frozen manure stack in front of it. Outside the sun shone. Inside the hut it was dark. The tiny window panes were covered by icicles. In the room a woman sat there, leaning against the wall of the brick kitchen stove. It was obvious there was no fuel to warm the place, not even a few sticks to start a fire. All was silence. I saw no traces of a cooked meal or any forms of preparing even a meagre one. The woman was breast-feeding a baby; not so much a breast as a sort of yellow sac made of human skin. The baby was blue, its eyes closed, probably asleep. The woman spoke indistinctly, something about a headache, feeling sick, had a pain somewhere. Taking note of this frozen emptiness and silence, I asked her when she last ate. The woman mumbled something about her old man who went out to dig out some potatoes. I did not ask whose potatoes, that's none of my business, most probably he went out to steal them. I suspended my rational reaction and gave the woman money to buy some bread, and prescribed cod liver oil for the baby, aspirin and other medication (glicerofosfat[3]) for her. Even the dog did not bark when I left.

This air of silence and indifference so affected me that I felt I was standing in an old, forgotten cemetery. I was reminded of the medieval atmosphere so admirably painted by the artist Breughel I saw in the Vienna art gallery. Winter. Frost and snow as far as eye could see. Frost and snow in peasant huts. Frost and snow in our hearts who can neither feel nor comprehend this poverty. Perhaps all peasants led similar lives throughout the world in the Middle Ages, but at the present time they lead them right here in our country.

Note 3: Glycerophosphate, a treatment for nutritional deficiency including rickets

Easter

A trip of 15 km. by car on roads of mud, puddles and pot-holes. The car is solid, the driver good and experienced, but in spite of this I am shaken to the core, I can feel my heart rising up to my throat. These are no longer the days when, at the beginning of my practice, I could run six kilometres on foot in order to send a patient to the hospital for an emergency operation. This is the eighth year of trips on mud, potholes and sand and I am beginning to feel the strain. Eight years of work, day and night, and already my heart is playing up. My legs shake as I get out of the car.

I'm told the patient I've been called out to see has been treated for TB. The hut where she lives is covered by wooden boards. It is surrounded by a small fence and behind it, right in front of the cottage windows stand stacks of manure probably to be used when spring comes. Next to the cottage is a cellar for storing potatoes, a tree trunk on which to chop wood, a dog in a kennel, and dreadful mud, mud, and more mud everywhere.

I enter the hut, cross a narrow corridor, open the door to the main room and am instantly overcome by nausea as a truly awful smell hits me. On the floor, on the chairs, on the table, lie pieces of a skinned animal, pig or ox, greenish yellow and slimy.

"What are you making?" I asked the man who appeared to be doing something with them.

"Guts for Easter blessings," [4] he replied.

In the district of Poznań they say 'guts' meaning 'sausage' (we would call them chitterlings).

The tripe and entrails were already in a separate bowl. I feel I would not be able to stand this suffocating air for long. On seeing these Easter "delicacies" I felt I might be sick.

"Where is the sick woman?" I managed to ask.

The man pointed to the corner. The patient was lying under a traditional eiderdown in the very same room, currently converted to a

Note 4: Easter blessings is a Polish tradition. On the Saturday preceding Easter Sunday baskets filled with small samples of food intended for the Easter big meal, are brought to the church to be blessed by the priest.

butcher's shop. The head of the flayed animal was under the bed.

The woman spits phlegm. I suspect she tuberculates. Temperature 38.5°C. There is a whole orchestra of rumbles and whistles in her lungs. Oh, those *"guts"* are going to be so good, so healthy, not to mention all that meat the Polish peasant consumes at Easter time.

Taking into account the possibility of spreading infection and the serious condition of the patient I wanted to send her to the hospital straight away. She refused, saying she's not going to spend Easter alone in the hospital.

"You can take me to the hospital after Easter, doctor," she said. "Right now I am not going, and that's that."

I tried to explain she might be infecting others, I criticised the way they were making those sausages. But the more I fulminated against that *'green meat'* being stored in a barrel waiting to be consumed at Easter, the more both she and her husband looked lovingly at their beloved *"guts"*. What was I to do? Call a policeman, destroy their good mood and their confidence?

I decided to wish them a *'Happy Easter'*.

And now for the horror

I was called out to the village of C. to a woman in childbirth. My driver complained about the difficult road. The road between S. and the village C. was steep, one my driver particularly disliked as it was covered with sludge and sticky mud. At that time there was no paved road leading to it. Somehow, laboriously, in first gear only for two kilometres, we managed to reach the village. The driver stopped at the nearest cottage, got out of the car and asked a group of people standing by: "Where does the sick woman live?"

The people looked at me with suspicion, even though they knew who I was. All the same, they whispered among themselves, dubious expressions on their faces. After a while they reluctantly pointed to a hut on a side road outside the village. The hut was of wood painted white, mud all around it, in the yard chickens and a dog, – everything as usual for these parts.

The room was tiny and dirty, at least half of it taken up by a wooden bed on which lay a young girl, scarcely developed, perhaps sixteen.

31

She had given birth the day before.

An old man with a long moustache, uneasy and agitated, pointed to the sick girl's cracked nipples. He was anxious about the baby and asked me how to feed it. I told him what to do and prescribed medication. I asked him whether a midwife was present at the birth and why was she not visiting the mother?

The old man, a labourer employed in the local brick factory, hence entitled to medical care for his daughter, said nothing. I guessed the baby was illegitimate; perhaps there were some complications, maybe legal ones. My visit over, I asked no more questions and left.

Outside there were more people standing around the car than usual. They whispered and talked among themselves. On our way back the driver said to me:

'Those people were telling me that old man had a child with his own daughter."

Ten years later I talked about such matters with a sociologist who was studying the living conditions of peasants in that district. He told me incest was far from rare among them. There were villages where around 10% of all children were born from such liaisons.

What sorts of people are being born in our new independent Poland?!

Emergency Cases

"Oh Lord, oh Lord, my man he screams and screams. Save him doctor!" a village woman burst into my consulting room during morning hours, anxious and upset.

"Where is that man of yours?" I asked, at the same time trying to decide what to take with me.

"Ah, in the village of W.S."

"Any chance of transport, any horses available?"

"How can it be, it's harvest time now."

I dealt quickly with the waiting patients and ran as quickly as I could to W.S. I found a fairly athletic-looking man in bed, moaning loudly. Pulse rapid, stomach hard as a board. I ran even more quickly back to S. to telephone for an ambulance. The patient had to be operated on instantly.

After about a month he arrived at the clinic to thank me personally (a fact I came across rarely in my practice in Warsaw). It was a case of a stomach rupture. Thanks to my *"gallop"* he was operated on just in time. My visit to see him and the 6 km run, lasted less than 40 minutes.

Oh the young, healthy heart of a beginner doctor! You are capable of breaking speed records. These days I would not be able to run six kilometres. It would end by calling an ambulance for the doctor. And it only happened a mere ten years ago.

*

The beautiful river Varta gave me a number of unpleasant shocks caused by cases of drowning. I was called to deal with those brought on land whom the rescuers were unable to resuscitate. On the whole I couldn't either. My visits in those cases were of the strictly formal kind. All I had to do was to write out a death certificate.

I remember one incident – a tiny fisherman's hut on the edge of the river. Inside, on the floor, lay a stout man with a black beard, dressed in black. He had drowned the previous day. Now they brought in his body and called me to fill in the form. This was my first death certificate I had to deal with. I had to fill in a great number of questions. What a difference between doing an autopsy in the company of colleagues and having to do it alone, on a dead person I knew, even though casually, in normal circumstances.

The wife of the dead man was crying her eyes out sitting outside this tiny hut. I was left alone with the dead man, laboriously examining his body for causes of death. It was obvious the man got very scared in his last moments; his face still bore traces of fear. The whole place was pervaded by a strange atmosphere. This tiny hut, the windows curtained off, the lit candles dimly breaking up the darkness of the room, all this affected me. I was gripped by fear.

I left the room with great relief. Once outside, neither the splendid, sunny weather nor even the beauty of the river could calm me down.

*

About one and half kilometres from my apartment was a factory making flares employing mostly women. The work was very dangerous because the materials used were easily combustible and fires a common occurrence.

One day I was called to an accident caused by an exploding flare.

33

On the factory floor lay an unconscious woman surrounded by pools of water. The woman's eyebrows and eyelashes were burnt, the skin on her face swollen and dark. She was deeply unconscious, her pulse weak. I gave her a stimulant injection for the heart. Just then an ambulance arrived to take her to the hospital in Poznań. She died shortly afterwards.

*

Very often I was called to issue a medical certificate to be presented in court cases. To obtain one people would come any time of day or night. They turned up with lacerations on heads, bruises on faces, and other incredible injuries inflicted on various parts of the body. Fights were quite common, usually at weddings, christenings and other festive occasions. People came to see the doctor as a last resort. Once the warring factions had sorted out their differences, they normally tried to treat each other. They would drench wounds in iodine, drawing on their war experiences, and then those involved would usually forget those stormy quarrels and forgive each other.

Two categories of losers demanded doctor's certificates needed for legal action. They were quite willing to pay even more for them than for a medical consultation. In the first category were participants of conflicts resulting from problems of accommodation - owners of houses, tenants and sub-tenants. The second had to do with family feuds, such as a husband badly beaten by a wife, or the other way round.

I attended to those various injuries, the cost covered by the Healthcare Fund, but I wonder if this should be so. Surely this could not be included under the category of casualties of workplace casualties. But you'd need a lawyer to sort out what happened, where and to whom, and I had no means to figure out how the law would apply.

*

During the period of my practice I only witnessed one attempted suicide, in the following circumstances.

A woman came to see me complaining of insomnia. The kind of complaint for which a doctor can only take a patient's word. I could not investigate whether a patient slept at night or not, unless they were under special observation.

The woman seemed very quiet and looked exhausted. I prescribed for her some mild sleeping pills. I was aghast when on the next day I was told by another woman that:

"Mrs. W. went to bed yesterday at 4 o'clock in the afternoon and hasn't woken up."

The patient lived in the village of G. four kilometres away. I managed to hire a horse-drawn cart and went to see her. She was deeply asleep, eyes half closed, pulse weak. Next to her bed lay an empty bottle of the prescribed pills. She had swallowed them all in one go. I counted the tablets and realised with relief that even if all had been taken together, the dose would not have been fatal. Nevertheless she had to be woken up because I was afraid of possible kidney complications. I gave her a stimulant heart medication and sent her to hospital in Poznań. After a week she returned home fully recovered. I asked her why she took the overdose, but received no clear answer. I suspected some mental illness. I was also afraid she might attempt to harm herself in more effective ways. But the woman did not come to see me again and I have heard nothing since.

Alcoholism in the country

In the villages covered by my practice I saw relatively few drunks. Probably the people did not have enough money to spend on alcoholic drinks, the poverty among the farm labourers was such there was simply no money to buy a bottle of vodka.

One contemptible exception was the village of D. with a distillery. I treated a cartwright who lived there. He was always busy, employed full time, never required any medical treatment. When eventually he did come to see me, under pressure from his wife, I discovered evidence of advanced heart failure combined with an enlarged heart and liver. He also suffered from emphysema and coughed a lot. In himself he looked cheerful and self-assured. Self-assured people one meets in villages rarely, and so this jolly cartwright stuck in my memory.

On his next visit to me I noted advanced deterioration in his health. I was amazed this man could walk and still work and, above all, be cheerful. In order to force him to stay in bed if only for a few days I decided to scare him and told him what I thought about his state of health.

"You will soon die if you don't stay in bed. Frankly I should send you

35

to the hospital." An experienced doctor should not tell a patient such things, but in this case I saw no other way.

"You never know who is the first to go," was the cartwright's reply. I could smell alcohol on his breath.

I continued to visit the village of D. from time to time, usually in the afternoon. I would find him tipsy, because it was his habit to have a drink with his meal. However, ever since that last conversation, feeling perhaps somewhat ashamed of his rude remark, he stopped coming to see me.

A month later I was in the village of D. seeing my patients when I remembered the cartwright.

"How is he doing?" I asked my driver.

"He died a week ago."

Births, miscarriages, illegitimate children

In the *"Medical News"* dated 1 March 1938 I came across a survey conducted among doctors attending a one year hospital practice course. One of them wrote:

"During my medical studies there was only theory and very little practice. How can one begin to practise as a doctor in such circumstances? Would it not be better instead of churning out often irrelevant theories during the course, more opportunities were provided to meet the sick and the healthy in person? Apparently there are medical schools where the student will not obtain his diploma until he has participated in a number of cases ranging from surgical to laboratory. Having done such training he can then begin to practise with confidence."

When I began my medical practice twelve years ago I was in a better situation than the doctor who wrote this article. But when a midwife asked me to assist at a birth for the first time, I was reminded of the ironic words of one of my professors of gynaecology: "If at the beginning of your practice you are called to a woman in labour, give the husband money to get another doctor".

Luckily that first childbirth was easy, the pains were weak, the woman well built, so that my ministrations were limited to an examination and injections. We had a new arrival. I was able to follow this child and many others like him, through the first years of their lives when I inoculated them against measles, to the time when they went to school, the passage of time marked not by ticking off days on a calendar, but by watching them grow, aware that I had assisted their entry into the world.

But not all childbirths were that were easy.

Haemorrhages caused by botched abortions were very frequent. For a doctor the worst fear was infection. Fortunately I had the support of a clinic for women and a gynaecological clinic in Poznań 7 km. away, as I did not want to take the responsibility for cases for which doctors were frequently taken to court. But a haemorrhage does not wait, life seeps away with every passing minute. Often I had to act quickly. On the whole, luck was on my side and my sick patients recovered without complications setting in.

I felt I could do with extra training in obstetrics. My husband, a surgeon in a military hospital, offered to take over my practice during his holiday. I approached a professor of gynaecology in Poznań who agreed to take me on at a well-run obstetrics and midwifery clinic attended by many doctors, particularly from the provinces. It was a combination of general medicine, surgery, childbirth and general commotion. One could learn a lot there. However, gynaecology did not appeal to me. I already knew enough from my experience in running a general practice and all I wanted was to supplement my knowledge in practical obstetrics which I considered absolutely necessary. I learnt what I needed there and I left after three months.

I observed the local customs with great interest. On the whole an engaged couple had already consummated their relationship. A number of young, pretty girls came to me complaining their periods had stopped. From my diagnosis whether they were pregnant or not depended whether they should start thinking about publishing banns in the church, or if they could wait. Often they would help themselves by resorting to abortion. I was unable to discover how they did it, or who carried it out, as the number of my patients grew to five a day. I repeat, folk medicine blossomed in the district. These 'enlightened people' drank herbal infusions (actually made from herbs of known medicinal properties), or used pins, pokers and similar tools.

In spite of many miscarriages a number of illegitimate children were born. At the time German laws still applied in the district of Poznań and every illegitimate child was put in the care of the municipal council. The council paid the so-called *'town sisters'* who registered these illegitimate children and supervised their living conditions. In S. these children were not treated badly. The father-fiancé was always regarded as a future husband, and only unfortunate conditions would prevent the couple from marrying. These *"unfortunate conditions"* were unemployment, or young age (around 18). Also before the wedding the municipality paid for the child, but after the wedding who was to pay for the child's maintenance?

The prejudices of the parents of the couple also played a part in making a marriage difficult. The son of a half-educated administrator in a soap factory was not given permission to marry the mother of his child because she was the daughter of a peasant on a couple of acres of land. I witnessed a number of such family quarrels and tried as much as I could to defend the fate of the little ones. I even invited engaged couples where pregnancy was diagnosed for counselling.

One of the most common gynaecological problems was a perineal tear after a birth resulting in a prolapse. I suspect this was the result not only of inadequate care during labour, but also of women's extremely hard work. In this district women had to carry heavy loads, they washed and scrubbed which meant they had to carry buckets of water. Apart from that, a labourer either owned or rented a piece of land. While he worked in a factory the women and children had to carry water to the fields, dig and weed then having collected the potatoes carry them in sacks on their backs. There were no draught animals; they had to do all the work. It is not surprising they suffered from prolapses.

Hysterical disorders in country women were exceptionally rare. I compare them with the wives of Warsaw factory workers, particularly those who came to see me privately. Some of the latter considered themselves fully blown *"ladies"*. A *"lady"* meant visits to a hairdresser, a manicure, and an ailment of some sort. *"I can lie on a sofa and be unwell"* was their scene.

But going back to those I looked after in the villages. I have no statistics, but based on my practice I can state that even though gynaecological ailments were fairly common, they were usually caused by badly carried out postnatal care or abortions gone septic. Inflammations, gonorrhoea, cancer- I came across those rarely.

A cry in the night

At that time I was still a young doctor prepared to get up at night when called to visit the sick. However, on that particular night, the first day of Christmas, I would have preferred a good night's sleep. My little son was only two months old.

Around two in the morning I was woken up by terrified crying outside my door. My servant opened the door. It turned out that a woman was in labour right in front of my door. A dishevelled man had brought her to me. He told me they were both unemployed and homeless. During the summer months they wandered from place to place looking for work in the fields. Now, in the winter they were living in a haystack outside the village of M. You cannot give birth in a haystack! The man had heard there was a doctor in S. and brought this homeless woman to my doorstep The railway station was only a short distance from my apartment. They telephoned for emergency services. The woman convulsed with pain and crying loudly, made her way slowly to the ambulance. Just before it pulled away she gave birth to a baby. I gave her some of my son's nappies and vests.

That was my Christmas in 1926.

Infectious diseases

The Social Insurance scheme together with progress in medicine brought a great deal of help in the field of infectious diseases. Each season of the year brought with it particular ailments to the villages covered by my practice. Towards the end of spring and early summer it was diphtheria, scarlet fever and all kinds of gastro-intestinal disorders. Around 50% of all ailments were in that category. In autumn and winter it was influenza, throat infections and pneumonia. Am I able to describe in detail these cases repeated a thousand times each year? Most of my time was primarily involved in dealing with them.

In S. people were very prone to throat infections. The town was situated near the river and maybe that had a bearing on their prevalence. I often met with cases of various forms of tonsillitis, quinsy (abscesses at the back of the throat) and diphtheria. Whenever I was called to see a child, I always made sure to take with me a supply of the anti-diphtheria serum.

To diagnose diphtheria in its early stages is very difficult without the back-up of bacteriological tests. Difficult access to Poznań discouraged sending swabs for microscopic examination and having to wait for the results. I would give anti-diphtheria serum injections, including prophylactic ones, without them.

There was one incident which will stay with me for the rest of my life. At the beginning of my practice I visited a four year old boy. I examined his throat very carefully and noted a slight reddening and nothing else. Next day, when I went to see him he was blue and had difficulty in breathing, but showed only a slight grey film in his throat. I injected a large dose of serum, but it did not help to save the child. Those throat infections shocked me.

I must have saved around a thousand children from such bacterial infections. In spite of that record I am not proud of it nor am I able to congratulate myself. That one incident at the beginning of my practice gave me such a shock that even subsequent numerous words of thanks from grateful patients fail to give me satisfaction. Always I think to myself – I have the best intentions, I try to keep up with new developments in medicine, but in the final count recovery is in the hands of nature, fate and, let's face it, the patient himself.

A throat abscess

The road from S. to the village W. was very sandy during the summer and one can only travel on it very, very slowly for 8 km along the grooves made by carts. Horses were borrowed and sent for me so I knew it was a serious case. I finally managed to reach W. in the summer heat, in the dust, along the banks of my beloved river.

A woman worker in the yeast factory was suffocating. At the back of her throat I saw an abscess the size of a small apple. Her pulse was racing, temperature 40°C., condition serious. I suggested incising the abscess. The sick woman was afraid, absolutely determined not give me her consent, saying she did not want to go to the hospital, and would rather die with no pain.

I didn't understand what she meant by 'no pain', and considered other options. The abscess had been forming for four days during which the woman did nothing about it. I decided to advise intense gargling and putting on a compress, hoping the abscess would burst on its own.

Having prescribed the medication I left with instructions to notify me in the evening about her state of health, particularly if she continued to suffocate. Nobody came that evening with news about her. Those were my early days of practice and if I did not hear from my patients, I always worried they might have died. I was always anxious about the human life given into my care and spent nights wondering did I do the right thing, did I prescribe the right medication. I had a great number of books only on treatments, but I had had enough of theoretical medicine.

The next day someone arrived from the village W. just to ask me to fill out a sick note for the duration of my patient's illness, because the abscess burst of its own accord three hours after I left. At least something like a quarter of a litre of pus came out and the patient went back to work, but needed the required certificate. She was sick for 5 days. Although she only called for me on the fifth day I knew she had been sick for four. Her unusual hurry to go back to work after such a serious incident confirmed she was certainly not malingering!

The "rash"

I was called to an estate owned by very good friends of mine, Mr & Mrs M. The living quarters of the farm workers were of brick, neat and clean. The owners themselves were personally involved in running the farm, so there were none of the abysmal sanitary conditions found in those run by administrators.

The family B. occupied not one room, but two. When I arrived I was shown a four year old child covered in pustules and red spots, eyes

41

swollen. It was *"the rash"* – a colloquial name for measles.

They showed me another child, a 6 year old. The same story. Two girls, age 12 and 14 were lying in the next bed, again showing the same symptoms. Even before I had a chance to turn around they showed me another boy. I rubbed my eyes.

"What's going on?" I asked. "Is this a hospital? All of you having the "rash"! How come there is so many of you?"

The walls were lined with beds made from wooden boards, filled with straw. In each there was on average two persons.

"How many of you are here?"

"There'll be twenty-four of us altogether."

"What?! Twenty-four!"

"Ah well, Dad was married twice and had twenty-two children."

At the present time 'only' nine had contracted the measles. Only nine! I would not have believed it if I had not seen it for myself.

Give them even slightly improved living conditions and it just goes to show what our village people are capable of!

The 1929 Influenza epidemic

During my practice in S. the epidemic coincided with two unusual events – an exceptionally hard frost combined with heavy snowfall and the so-called *'No-Contract'* situation between the Medical Union and the Healthcare Fund in Poznań.

The *'No Contract'* or, as it was commonly referred to as the *'Doctors' strike'*, was the result of long payment delays by the Healthcare Fund. The Medical Union had difficulty negotiating with the *'Sick Fund'* and instructed the doctors to collect payment directly from their patients. Those payments were set only slightly higher than those the Healthcare Fund paid the doctors. I don't remember the exact figures, but I think we were paid 1.50 zloty per visit at the practice and 5 zloty per home visit.[5] The Healthcare Fund set up a sort of a bank account. Every insured person applying to his selected doctor for a Healthcare card could receive for himself, his wife and children 3 zloty

Note 5: Present day value 2.5zl=£5.10; 5zl=£10.20

to use for medical cover. Some of the insured supported five or more family members. When one of them fell ill, he would apply to the Healthcare Fund and receive medical cover for all the members. With the money thus obtained the one who was actually sick would go to see a doctor and pay them, while the rest of the money would be regarded as a refund of the fee. Clearly that state of affairs could not last. The Healthcare Fund could not support such outgoings and its budget was in a very poor state. After eighteen months of 'No-Contract' it entered into new negotiations with the Medical Union, resulting with a new contract being drawn up.

In 1929 the 'flu epidemic in S. was raging. I am left only with snippets of remembered incidents. My journeys to the villages to see the sick involved enormous difficulties. During that time I worked sixteen hours a day, and could only have done it thanks to a reliable car. In order to reach the villages required chains on tyres, two spades to dig us out of the snow and planks to put under the wheels. A journey of eight kilometres took between 2-3 hours. In the daytime I would make 25 to 30 visits. Around fifteen people at any one time were down with 'flu. I still remember the cold, dark rooms, the dirty eiderdowns under which lay steaming bodies, as the high temperature which accompanies the 'flu causes intensive sweating.

On my return, when it was getting dark, I would be seeing the sick in my consulting room. I can't remember how many kilograms of aspirin and other anti-flu medications I prescribed during those cold winter months. All this felt like a field hospital during a war – 24 hours on duty, 12 hours rest, repeated again and again.

Somehow I managed. I do not remember anyone dying of the 'flu, and complications resulting from it were very rare.

Malingering

The red tape a doctor has to deal with affected the relationship between a doctor and a patient. In the Healthcare Fund in the district of Poznań the bane of my practice were the malingerers. They "travelled" from one doctor to another, sniffing out who was an easy touch for sick notes for which the Healthcare Fund had to pay. I suspect they considered me sympathetic to their simulated illnesses because a fair number of them came to see me.

The temptation to malinger was the result of high rates of Healthcare Fund benefits. Factory workers in 1927-1930 earned good money. At the same time, in S. for instance, they also owned small plots of land. When it was the season to work on the land, or if temporary offers cropped up, they would feign illness in order to obtain sick leave from their factory job.

In the system of Social Insurance the severity of an illness had to be confirmed by a GP. It had a negative effect on the doctor/patient relationship. Nowadays a patient has to be forced to remain in bed until he has completely recovered, to stop him going back to work. In those days patients would unjustifiably extend their sick leave. Symptoms of the 'flu last on average four to five days. In the previous system of paying out the benefits it would have been extended to ten days. I do not remember what rates Healthcare Fund paid for severe illnesses, but I do remember numerous appeals issued by the Medical Union and the Healthcare Fund to check if the severely ill patients were actually in bed. In my experience I had countless unpleasant incidents. I remember one during that time of severe frost and snowdrifts. I was called to a patient to the village D. about 10-12 km. from S. My car had just broken down, so I said that they will have to send the horses if I have to visit, but only if the condition of the sick person was critical.

The horse drawn cart duly arrived the next day and I went through snowdrifts for 12 km. On arrival I saw the sick woman in bed – a village girl with smooth complexion and normal temperature. I could not find any signs of an illness. When they demanded that I fill in their claim form for sickness benefit which was to state she was severely ill, I refused and was met with grumbling and protests.

"So why did we send the horses for you? All that trouble for nothing."

"Why is she pretending to be ill, if there is nothing wrong with her?"I replied.

"She lost two days at work and we want to claim benefits from the Healthcare Fund. That's what our neighbour advised us to do. He could've spared us that kind of advice."

It was obvious some cheat told the ignorant village woman how to

44

manipulate the Healthcare Fund, something the woman did not quite grasp. I believe the girl did not lose her job; she just found it exhausting to walk to the factory during that spell of frost and snowdrifts.

Generally speaking, certification of a severe illness form went like this: I would fill in my diagnosis and the period expected to be off work on the Social Insurance sickness form with my name as the doctor and a stamp of validity for four weeks. Later we were provided with already printed separate forms. The sick person's family had to go the next day to the Healthcare Fund to declare the sick person's inability to go to work. This was compulsory; it meant loss of benefits if they did not do this. One could post these certificates. The Healthcare Fund then sent their inspector to check the severity of the illness. Inspectors were people with little or no medical experience and often not much intelligence either. Admittedly, they were only required to check whether the sick person was in bed and not at work.

Doctors were also required to check on the severely ill patients. The control, in my opinion, was badly organised, based from the very beginning on faulty premises. Either I am a doctor hence able to visit the sick and make a diagnosis, or I cannot be trusted. This kind of check on the person whose certificate I have signed should be accepted on trust. I followed the instructions and would make unannounced visits at varying times. There were occasions when sick patients did go to work, or were not at home. This was not always because they were not as seriously ill as they claimed. A man with TB and high temperature did get out of bed, though not supposed to, because he needed to attend a court hearing. Since I did not find him at home I was obliged to mark him as *'able to work'*. There was an instance of a person deemed able to work who died the next day. Fortunately I did not have a case like that, but they did occur, evaluated later by the medical commission.

New rules introduced in 1934 removed this particular duty. Eliminating this kind of abuse was, in my opinion, a big forward step in the development of Social Insurance.

45

Tuberculosis

By my estimate a considerable number of consultations were devoted to those with the symptoms of TB. Out of the 100,000 or so consultations conducted by me during my working life, I believe at least a fifteenth of my patients, particularly those from S. were consumptive. At this moment this disease reminds me of one of the monsters I saw on the roof of the cathedral of Notre Dame in Paris. With its steady gaze, protruding lips, dangling, dog-like ears, it stares unflinchingly at the world. Whoever is caught within its line of vision is doomed. The shocking images of the slow process of dying and finally the death of young consumptives I had to watch forced me to seek in my imagination those legendary monsters in order to somehow personify their suffering.

If we work hard and are alert making an early diagnosis then, generally speaking, we might be able to help those afflicted with the disease. Very often however this does not happen, and in spite of the best will in the world, we are unable to help given our present knowledge. I stress this on purpose because faced with a doctor's helplessness I was aware of the patients' instant, reproachful reaction. The simple people, the peasants, the labourers were simply unable to comprehend that in cases of advanced TB the outcome was hopeless. They would leave my consulting room perhaps with some acceptance that no more could be done only to enrol as patients of quacks, herbalists, *"wise, old women"* and masseurs.

However well prepared and with the best will in the world there was nothing a doctor could do to help the patient.

The village people I looked after for 8 years sometimes understood this. Often I heard the country proverb: "Once you caught death, a doctor can save his breath".

There were instances when from the very beginning I was able to predict the outcome of a disease and file it under the heading: *"Death"*. This happened particularly in the cases of TB. Obviously I never used that word when talking to a patient who, while fighting for his life, would anyway be cursing the doctors unable to defeat it.

At present, in the majority of cases an early diagnosis results in a better outcome. There is no doubt that Social Insurance gets excellent results in treating this disease. Without its support how could a young labourer, or his wife, afford a stay for 2-3 months in a sanatorium, or in hospital undergoing various treatments? People got so used to its availability they no longer appreciate its value. Only the farm labourers who lost their insurance can appreciate the support of the Social Insurance, particularly in combating TB.

With no Social Insurance in the rural districts, a doctor is called in only in terminal cases. Anyway, a farm labourer has no money to pay the doctor, and employers, unwilling to cover the cost of treatment, will only finance medical care as the last resort.

At the end of a narrow street stood a small, wooden house half-sunk into the ground from old age, covered with a straw-thatched roof. Two dogs barked loudly when for the first time I came to visit a sick young woman living there. The room was very damp. The young woman was lying under a heap of eiderdowns emitting a characteristic smell of sweat. Her temperature 39 degrees C., in her lungs a whole orchestra of reverberations and whistles.

"Why didn't you call me earlier?" I asked.

"They were all a bit weak since they were little," said the mother of the sick woman.

"You do realise your daughter has TB."

The woman said nothing, just stared vacantly into space.

The patient's condition was such there was no point in admitting her to hospital or a sanatorium. She died ten days later.

I reported it to the Public Health office. They disinfected the house.

Two weeks later the dead woman's brother came to my consulting room with congestion in his left lung. After several examinations I sent him to a sanatorium. Some months later I was called again to that small, thatched house. The sick man was lying in the same bed as his sister who died six months ago. His eyes were huge and shiny, temperature around 40 deg. C. He was so thin he looked like a skeleton.

"It's nothing, I'm all right," he said. "In the sanatorium they gave me injections and medicines, but I just can't eat. Please give me something to make me eat."

After a thorough examination I diagnosed acute miliary tuberculosis. All his internal organs as well as his lungs were affected.

47

"I don't want to die, I want to live. Have you no medicine for what's ailing me?" he cried desperately, condemned to a slow death.

It turned out that after he had discharged himself from the sanatorium and returned to S., he was treated by a whole team of local village helpers. A *"military doctor"* even prescribed a special medicine for him, not like the one he could get from the Healthcare Fund, because there they trick you and what you get from them is rubbish. After that *'curative'* visit, a wise old woman was called. The old woman burned incense, applied magic, spat into the four corners of the world while mumbling incantations. She gave the sick man a broth from a black cock killed at midnight. Even that did not help and so the patient finally called me.

The unhappy man was fully aware that his life draining away and of his slowly approaching death. This awareness is the worst thing to happen to those in his situation. I prescribed medication to help him sleep, but he still could not eat. The tuberculosis of the intestine was ruining his body. I continued to visit him for ten days, only to sign the death certificate on the eleventh.

I looked carefully at the old woman, his mother.

"How many children have you buried already?" I asked.

It finally turned out that her husband and four children, ages from eighteen to twenty-four had died from TB in the last six years. The woman did not want to reveal the fact two of her older children had died of it when I first called.

"This house ought to be pulled down. You should leave this place," I said. "Have you any more children?"

"Just one married daughter. She lives in the village of K."

"What's her name?"

"Sobczak."

I nearly jumped. Only the day before I was in K. where I visited Mrs. Sobczak and diagnosed TB.

"And you, how do you feel, are you well?"

The woman waved her hand dismissively. Only she, the mother of children who had all died of TB was free of it.

After the funeral of the last child the house became empty. What could a simple peasant woman do there? All her life she was surrounded

48

by a numerous family and now she was the only one left. What did she think about when that cruel, pitiless disease swept them all away?

I felt like hanging a black flag over this household.

*

The young man worked in the district chemical factory, in the soap manufacturing section. The little house where he lived was situated near the factory, by the river Varta. It was built of brick and very clean. When I first visited him I diagnosed 'flu. When called two days later I made a note of my diagnosis – lung investigation required. The patient brought the X-ray results on the third visit . They were short and to the point – early TB, catarrh of the upper lobes.

He was twenty-two years old, had done his military service. Nobody in his family had TB, or any members of his household. He was an amiable man, intelligent, an avid reader. The slightly raised temperature persisted, but he continued to refuse my suggestions to go to the sanatorium or a hospital.

"I have to go to work tomorrow or I'll lose my job." His reply was always the same. I tried to persuade him to take a rest.

"Your temperature is 37.5 deg. C at midday, what will it be in the afternoon or evening? If you continue to go back to work, what do you think might happen?"

I only managed to keep him indoors for ten days. I did not spare cod liver oil, calcium and every possible injection to build up his strength. I noted a slight, slow improvement, and after three months he stopped coming to see me. That was in February. In July I was called urgently to a case of lung haemorrhage in the chemical factory, only to find out it concerned my patient. He had already been sent home.

I found him in bed under a traditional eiderdown. There was blood in the bucket next to the bed. The young man was pale and very frightened. This is usually the case with haemorrhages; it induces a state of shock. I prescribed ice, injections and rest. I could do no more, just tried to cheer him up.

"Think of yourself as if made of glass – you are not to talk or move. Just go to sleep for half an hour, and when you wake up all will be well."

When I visited him the next day he began to talk very quietly.

"You always told me to go out into the fresh air. I was lying by the

49

river in the shade and fell asleep. The sun came out. I slept for three hours. When I woke up my mouth was full of blood."

High temperature was beginning to set in. With each day the patient became more and more skeletal. Ribs, hand and ankle joints protruded from deep depressions covered by the skin. The patient called for me almost every day. I suffered terribly watching him slowly die. I prescribed narcotics to reduce his suffering.

To watch this slow process of young people dying of pulmonary tuberculosis fully aware they are dying coupled with a great desire to live, is the cruellest aspect of a doctor's life.

*

When I first came to S. I paid a visit to the upper echelons of the town's society. Mr X was one of the first. I had to wait for a long time for him to return my visit. He was a Poznań man through and through, and did not like new arrivals, the 'strangers'.

One night, I was woken up at three in the morning. Mr X's sister was haemorrhaging.

The lady worked in the post office, so she was covered by the Healthcare Fund. I went quickly to Mr.X's house where I found panic and dismay. There was this young, pretty girl and right now she was haemorrhaging from the lungs! Nobody in the family was thought to have TB.

All kinds of medication, calming the patient, and such like, brought about the required result. She stopped haemorrhaging. But the treatment had to be continued. After a great number of intravenous injections of calcium and other medicines the sick girl was well enough to go to a sanatorium to continue her treatment there. Finally, it ended well. When she returned from the sanatorium she was the picture of health. She returned to work travelling by train to the office and I had the lovely opportunity to admire her recovery from an illness which had given me great concern.

I thought then that maybe at long last those grudging people of S. will gain confidence in me as their doctor since I managed to cure a person of high standing in the town's hierarchy so effectively.

Work in the brickyard and in the artificial fertiliser factory

Around the town of S, as in all districts surrounding the city of Poznań, there were many brickyards. Carrying and transporting clay, as well as casting and firing the bricks was not only hard, unhealthy work, above all it was badly paid.

I don't know why a brickyard worker was paid less than in other factories. Because the rates were low, mostly women worked there. It was predictable that most of them would end up as my patients sooner or later. Exhaustion, a weakened heart associated with an enlargement of the left ventricle, swollen legs, were very common occurrences. But even more common was TB. My standard response was to send the sick women to a sanatorium where their health would markedly improve, only to relapse once they returned to work, unable to find another job anywhere else. Because they were mostly mature women the symptoms were not as aggressive as in the young. Generally speaking, after a period of medical treatment they would recover their health.

On the opposite bank of the river Varta, facing the artificial fertiliser factory was the village of Cz. I went there to visit a man who worked in that factory. He was about fifty and overweight. Suddenly he had become weak and started spitting blood. I remember the cottage where he lived very well. It stood by a sandy path just near the river bank. On the opposite side was the wood with its rustling branches, around it stretched the sands of the river banks. It didn't seem that the country around was conducive to TB, especially as none of his family had it. When I began to examine him I was told the following story.

"In our factory everyone gets sick after working there for about ten years. You begin to feel a bit weak...." At this moment my patient started to cough violently and showed me a blood clot which he spat into his handkerchief.

I noticed that fumes produced by these artificial fertiliser factories have a damaging effect on blood vessels supplying the lungs which subsequently burst.

It took me a long time to cure this patient. He did get better but did not go back to work in that factory. A sick pension would have a made a difference, but in those days workers were not insured.

51

About the young generation and amelioration of the rural districts

About a half of the inhabitants of the village of D. were German. The bailiff or perhaps the owner of the estate was German. There I was able to compare the cottages of the Poles with the German ones. Because both Poles and Germans were insured by the Healthcare Fund so all were my patients.

The Germans lived mostly in brick cottages, the Poles in wooden ones. I don't know whose houses they were; probably they all belonged to the estate, so perhaps it was not surprising the German gave his compatriots better houses than the Polish labourers. However, there was a marked contrast in their interiors and also in the state of the roads in front of them.

In front of the Polish cottages were small gardens surrounded by woven stick fences. In the winter piles of manure would be deposited right in front of the windows, waiting for Spring when they would be used as fertiliser. Towards the end of winter, in February, those piles were so high they almost covered the windows. There were cellars where potatoes were kept and their entrances too would be covered by stacks of manure. When one entered a room of such a cottage the stench was overpowering, because the air passing through gaps in the windows flowed over those continuously steaming manure heaps. Also, the road in front of those cottages was covered in manure and mud so that often they could not be reached by car. I then had to get out and walk, sinking in that awful mud, holding on to fences so as not to slip and fall into the mire.

In front of the German cottages I never saw any manure at all. Inside, the interiors were much cleaner and tidier. I was not able to explain the difference. The pay for farm labourers working on the same estate was surely not that different to enable some to maintain their houses in a clean state and reasonably well furnished, while others lived in dismal hovels, almost like pigsties.

I was about to describe my patients living in towns, but find it difficult to leave the country people. For me it was a pleasure to work among them, and I can count many "grateful patients". In retrospect, those people appeared so helpless and abysmally poor. I wanted to do anything, however small, to lighten their wretched existence. So I should like to say a few words about the young generation living in the country, those blond-haired little ones crawling on all fours among the manure heaps, fed on potatoes and little else almost from birth.

Right now I am seeing one little chap from a farm cottage. His legs are crooked, he is afraid of me, very shy and holds on to his mother's apron. Mother wipes his nose with her finger and lifts him up to enable me to examine him. His scalp is still soft, his belly distended, legs crooked caused by the *"English disease"*, the elegant name for rickets.[6] 90% of children of school age in the country are affected by it. It affects the development of the spine for the rest of their lives. As I was the only doctor in the district it is not surprising I had many opportunities to see cases of rickets. I undertook to examine and look after the children in the village schools. The council paid me the princely sum of 30 gr per child.[7] Having examined the children twice a year I noted in practically all of them an enlargement of neck glands under the jaw and considerable rib cage deformations, all the result of rickets. Among other diseases I often saw were scabies, rotten teeth and bronchitis. Active TB was rare, but enlarged glands were present in practically every child.

How many barrels of cod liver oil should have been sent to the villages, how many centres for mother and child set up in order to eliminate this dreadful plague?!

Our sociologists foresee a demographic decline in Poland. Their forecasts are confirmed by the drop of population in Poland from one year to the next. In my opinion a health awareness and educational campaign should be introduced very quickly. It would be a step towards eliminating the dreadful poverty presently existing in the rural communities caused not only by the lack of welfare support but, above all, the low educational level of our peasants. The rural population is poor and owns very little land. But even in those conditions they could live 50% better if they knew how to conduct their everyday life and how to work efficiently to reduce poverty. That village of mixed Polish and German population gave me food for thought.

I fully support the Memorandum on Rural Healthcare sent to the

Note 6: Severe vitamin D deficiency
Note 7: Around £1 in today's money

53

Minister of Social Care by the National Medical Chamber in January 1938. However, in my humble opinion, the standard of living of peasants will not be greatly improved if the legislation does not give more prominence to that miniscule fraction of society, the peasant family, than it does at present. If it doesn't, the Memorandum will not bring any positive results. As it stands, the new legislation applies only to healthcare, and the peasant population will carry on as before. What is needed is a wider holistic approach which would include all aspects of the life of a peasant and bring out his dormant strength. Until now a great deal of good will is being spent just on raising village sanitary conditions. An example of that is a directive to build separate-standing toilet facilities (the so-called sławojki named after the prime minister who initiated this scheme). As far as I am concerned this initiative is ridiculous. I appreciate the good intentions coming from 'above', but I also see the lack of enthusiasm from the people for whom it is intended.

The misunderstanding stems from the absence of a holistic system which would embrace the whole of our life; instead dealing only with today's issues and even then, just their fragments. Those fragments are tiny indeed. The rural population is indifferent to these reforms, as they feel that they are ill thought out and also that they have been put into place by those who rather than starting with the big issues, have started with the small and inconsequential. In consequence indifference sets in towards all top down reforms. The country people cannot understand why those who offer to help can only see the proverbial fly and miss the elephant. That is why the rural countryside fails to awaken and move forward.

Unemployment

Every doctor working in the community sooner or later gets involved in social welfare and I too found myself involved on a wider scale.

After five years as a medical practitioner in both the industrial and rural districts, I joined various women's and workers' organisations where I was given a responsible position. Living in S. made my social work difficult. I headed an organisation which had its branches in the whole Poznań province. My presence was needed in the office of the

54

organisation. I moved to the city and began to work on several fronts – still working for the Healthcare Fund in Poznań and the outlying districts, at the same time heading the women workers association, also acting as councillor, while continuing to visit patients in the outlying villages.

The province of Poznań was covered by the Healthcare Fund and this carried with it the free choice of doctor. This meant that when I moved back to Poznań I had to re-sit my GP exams. I don't know how or why but it all went smoothly and after just four months I was able to earn my living. Many patients registered with me, their number growing daily.

In Poznań I found a place to live in a district where there was an amusement park. Nearby, on the outskirts, were new buildings – rows of small houses, huts, dwellings inhabited during winter and summer months, built on a shoestring. The poor, the unemployed, and all kinds of "social rejects" formed a stream flowing to my consulting room, their doctor of choice. I was obviously popular among these people.

The times were getting worse; the period of relative prosperity was coming to an end, and a critical one beginning. Many workers were losing their jobs. During the period of full employment they built for themselves tiny houses outside the city, on mud, on the sands, among heaps of rubbish. As soon as they found employment even if only for a month they would come to see me. Women in particular understood the value of Social Insurance. They brought their children for check-ups and medication. They bemoaned the fact they could not continue their medication once the fathers became unemployed. They asked for cod liver oil. They were sorry to lose the right to the benefits because they were only temporarily employed.

The people in Warsaw reading this might suspect I am writing this for effect in this competition. I am writing this because that is the truth, and to stress – that's how it was in Poznań, not in Warsaw where the situation was completely different. I will mention this again, but right now I should like to draw attention to the importance of the Social Insurance in the Poznań province.

On my way to visit the villages I would stop at small cottages outside the city, built of clay and wattle, where my patients lived, mostly unemployed. TB there was rampant.

The Amusement Park

[The literal translation from the Polish is "Jolly town" which more accurately conveys the ironic twist to this story, so I am going to use it throughout – MC.]

On the 19th December 1934 at a meeting of the Poznań town council I presented the following submission:

After the National Fair in Poznań in 1929, around thirty families moved into the post-exhibition grounds over the course of two days unnoticed by the council, and took over the pavilions. Temporary partitions were erected creating in what is now called the "Jolly town". The families who moved there were evicted from private homes. The unemployed with their numerous families followed, also unmarried mothers with their children, women living alone, and men earning money by dubious means. They were joined by men who earned their money honestly but whose lack of housing forced them to seek the roof over their heads there.

Those who found a space by the windows although freezing cold as the flimsy walls let in considerable draughts, were in the lucky situation of having light and air. Worse off were the windowless dens built inside the big exhibition halls. Here the only ventilation came from the long, smelly corridors, or from windows in the ceiling. In one such den, an area three metres by four (ie 9 by 12ft). I found a family consisting of a chronically ill grandfather, a grandmother, the parents, and five children. The air was so overpowering that it made one dizzy and sick. As to the toilet facilities the least said the better.

In the "Jolly town" now live 2200 people, children and adults, altogether 750 families. The living conditions of the young generation there is more than dire. What kind of citizens will be living in our city in ten years' time, brought up in those conditions?"

I have copied here part of my submission which was duly acknowledged by the city of Poznań. I presented it also to the plenary assembly at a meeting of the Soviet club to which I belonged. Having so many poor under my care in the "Jolly town" made me bring it out into the open. Just mark this:

I am called to visit a woman, a newspaper seller, living in pavilion 281. It is on my way to the village of M. where I was visiting another patient. The year 1929 is remembered in that district of Poznań for the splendid Exhibition with its amusement arcades. Now, in this winter of 1934 it is a picture of poverty and despair. Stove pipes stick out from the once beautiful pavilions, covering the outside walls with soot. I keep tripping on piles of rubbish and rubble. There is no snow because winters in Poznań are not severe, but the air is so damp it produces a penetrating cold. I walk past old, broken masonry and am immediately surrounded by inquisitive and meddlesome children.

"Who are you seeing? I'll take you there. No, I'll take you."

There will always be someone who wants to sit next to the driver, go for a drive of few metres. Some of the children had never sat in a car. "Have you any sweets? Can you spare a coin?"

Finally two little kids triumphantly lead the way to the sick woman, seeming as if they have just found me.

At least thirty wooden lean-tos are attached to one of the walls of the huge hall. I enter one of them, and am seized by a dizzy spell and a wave of nausea, overcome by the smell of old shoes and old rags. The window faces the corridor and it lacks what a window is supposed to be for – to let in light and air. The woman's state is almost hopeless. Heart failure, massive oedema. Yet only a week ago she came to collect newspapers from the printers' office.

"I am sending you to the hospital, you cannot stay here," I tell her.

The woman refuses. She will lose her job if she goes to the hospital.

"But you are not working anyway," I say.

"Yes, but they don't know it. The children take the newspapers round for me."

"Well then, they can carry on doing that while you are in hospital."

"But children don't have the right. The staff only hand them out to adults."

What could I do? She did not go to the hospital and died eight days later. She had three children, three sons. All were illegitimate, with no resemblance to each other. The eldest was fifteen, the youngest eight. They had no other family. The city took care of them. I gave the eldest some money towards the funeral expenses.

The first generation of the worker intelligentsia

The father worked in a tannery. I remember him very well on account of a particular detail. He wore a leather jacket which had an overpowering, foul smell. Probably he absorbed it in the tannery, so that when he arrived straight from work and sat in my waiting room, the air became heavy and stifling. The man had a ruddy complexion which contrasted with his white moustache.

His son was studying law. A highly strung, tall, dark-haired man who came to see me. I diagnosed TB straight away, so far advanced it would not have been possible to miss it. It turned out he knew about his condition. He used to work in an institution of some kind and was able to claim the right to medical care. At present he was unable to work, (state medical care did not cover those who were not working), but as he was financially supported by his father he intended to take advantage of the thirteen weeks right to medical care as a family member. Supported by the Healthcare Fund I was able to send him to a sanatorium. He stayed there for the prescribed period and returned to Poznań. On the whole he felt well. Once the right to the Healthcare Fund expired he stopped coming to see me. He was then treated privately with some wondrous injections.

After a year, when again he had regained the right to medical care from the Healthcare Fund, I was called to see him. He lived with his parents in a newly built villa on the first floor. He continued to have fevers, but did not want to go to the hospital or to a sanatorium, so it was left to me to treat him as best I could. I was wondering where this young man had caught TB. His parents were both a picture of health though working hard, while he, a twenty-five-year old man, a university graduate, was ill. What a blow for the old couple!

His father, working in a tannery had scrimped and saved and used the money, not buy land or build a cottage as most workers earning reasonable wages did, but to educate his son to be lawyer. And just before graduation – an end like this! The young man studied hard, did not eat well. At first he didn't want to see a doctor and continued to work. When eventually he stopped he lost the right to medical care. His health deteriorated slowly.

The old man, his father, would come to see me for "private" advice, naturally free of charge. He spoke about his son, a university graduate, as though he and I were colleagues. I tried to help the best I could. All the medicine I had for his condition were passed on to him.

One day the old man came to see me with the following news.

"I found a doctor who promises to get him well. But he is asking 100zl.[8] for an injection. Madam Doctor, I need your advice. Should I give him that 100 zł.? That's all I have, that's the rest of my savings. But I want to save him."

What was I to do? I watched as tears dripped onto his white moustache.

"All I can say is that the medical profession has done all it possibly could in order to save your son. He was in a sanatorium where they spared no effort. It is obvious to me that someone is trying to deceive you. Do not believe in such miracles."

Five days later he returned, looking calm and composed as he asked me to sign the death certificate. He thanked me for warning him against this doctor. I said:

"Well, at least you kept your 100 złoty."

"No, I did give him the money. Only I see now you were right because my son has died."

Note 8: Present day value 1,700zl or £340

An economics exam.

One of my patients was a law student working in the Chamber of Commerce. I visited him at home when he was down with 'flu. He lived in a furnished room let by a landlady who, together with her daughter, were also my patients. I suspected he was not too keen to study. He was good at drawing and the walls of his room were covered by drawings of women in various activities and poses. He told me he was revising for his exams. Once he recovered I did not see him again and nearly forgot about him.

One summer he came to see me with a pained look on his face, his head held to one side. He was suffering from a cramp in the muscles of his neck and arm – so-called torticollis.

"What happened?" I asked. "Was it the draught?"

"No, this happened as the result of my examination. The Prof. went behind a screen, spread out some papers and asked me a lot of questions."

"And you found it disconcerting?"

"Yes."

"Well, and did you pass?"

"Yes, have a look."

I looked at the notes. They were marked: 'Try again', 'Just about right', 'Fair'.

If all students reacted to their marks in this way it would cost the Healthcare Fund a great deal of money.

Prompt action on my part together with medication removed all the adverse consequences resulting from taking an examination in economics.

Something's not quite right

I also had patients belonging to the Healthcare Fund from the more affluent part of the city. I was just called by a dressmaker who lived there albeit in an annexe, but still.

In her apartment stood a mannequin, a sewing machine, and all kinds of fabric and dresses spread on the table, the chairs and the sofa. The dressmaker, a very attractive young woman, was breastfeeding a baby. She complained about feeling exhausted and weak and looked quite upset.

'Maybe breastfeeding makes you feel exhausted?' I asked.

'Oh definitely,' she replied. *'To feed two babies is no joke. It's been six weeks since the birth. But I must go on working. It's the season.'*

'So you had twins ?' I asked.

I had treated her eldest daughter in the past – an exceptionally pretty young girl, a 16 year old 'Miss Mary' [9] who attended singing classes. Miss Mary had a cherubic face as long as she did not open her mouth. When she did her looks changed for the worse – she had bad

Note 9 This is an affectation. Normally in Polish it would be 'Maria' or a diminutive 'Marysia'

teeth and an unattractive facial expression. I had not seen her in the last six months or so.

"You, you are such a sympathetic doctor," the dressmaker was saying, "You must help us, or my husband will kill it."

"It? Who?"

"Ah this one," she pointed to the baby she was breastfeeding.

'What! Kill his own child?!'

"I got pregnant, and didn't feel well throughout the pregnancy. What I should've done is got rid of it. I already have two girls. But my husband always wanted a boy. I had a lot of work coming to me, I didn't leave the house. In my sixth month I noticed my Mary looking somehow different. "Daughter – I say to her, something's not quite right" – that's what I say to her. She says it's nothing. The worst part was when I was about to give birth. I was already feeling the pains and what I see is Mary in bed, panting. – "Daughter, I say to her, for God's sake, this isn't right. What's going on?"

My daughter gave birth to a boy . I told my husband it's mine and that I am expecting a second any time now, because the midwife told me I am having twins. My third daughter was born two days later. I registered them both as twins under my name. If it wasn't a boy I'd have probably suffocated the baby, but as it's a boy my husband is not that cross."

"I see. But how come your daughter is not breastfeeding the baby?"

The dressmaker gave me an indignant look.

"Mary is a young lady and if she spoils her figure her fiancé won't marry her."

I prescribed for her a tonic and got far away from that family saying nothing to anybody, neither to the police, nor to the father who so badly wanted a son. It remained a doctor's secret.

Attempts at blackmail

Thankfully they were only 'attempts'. It happened like this:

I received a telephone call from home while I was at a fairly stormy meeting of a certain organisation. A man had arrived at the house with a dreadful story. He said that his sister had dropped dead immediately after swallowing one pill which I had prescribed. For a thing like this to happen struck me as impossible. If, for instance, I did make a mistake and prescribed a dose which could have been fatal, the pharmacist was obliged to contact me and verify the doze. Apart from that, I was pretty sure I had not prescribed any fatal medicines. So I told the man to come and see me the next day at an arranged time.

The man, of dubious background, instantly demanded compensation. I asked for the name of the sick woman and a copy of the "poisonous" prescription. It turned out that the woman had once come to my practice. She was seen by my deputy-cum-locum Dr Z. who, having diagnosed anaemia, prescribed a very popular tonic and a phosphate medication. The man, however, only presented the death certificate of that patient six weeks after the visit. During those six weeks nobody called either asking for a visit, or to inform us that the medicine prescribed by my deputy-cum-locum had had such an adverse effect.

I asked the man to come back the next day. In the meantime I contacted the police in the patient's district, in order to find out who signed the death certificate, the cause of death, and whether it was unexplained or sudden. If the latter was the case, why was she buried without an autopsy?

The policeman on duty obviously knew all about it because very quickly and in great detail gave me the required information. Indeed the man, who said he was the patient's brother, did come to the police station to register the required report but only after the funeral. According to the police records the patient was registered under a different GP whom she saw with some gynaecological complaint. The death certificate was signed by a doctor in the A&E. There was no mention of any violent or sudden death. The prescription was passed to the Judicial Medical Council who stated that even if the woman took all the prescribed pills at once, all she might have ended with would have been a stomach ache. But allegedly, she dropped dead after taking only one! It was not worth anybody's time even to start court proceedings. As it happened, the inquest had already taken place even without my knowledge. So, when the patient's brother came to see me the next day I said: "Do not come and bother me again. If you persist with the complaint and demands for money it will only end badly for you."

After six months of peace I received a notification from the court that the mother of that patient wants to bring a malpractice suit against me. She wants to sue me for a mere…10,000 zl.[10] and is trying to obtain legal aid, so that the court proceedings would cost her nothing. I had to seek the advice of a lawyer. He wrote a suitable letter. I too, sent in my explanation. The blackmailer did not receive legal aid. Clearly, there was no merit in the case, because the blackmailer gave up and stopped pestering me.

Note 10: 10,000zl = present day value 170,000zl = £340,000

The Poznań children

Children – the sweetest little creatures on earth! Resolute and well behaved. In my recollections of the most remote districts of the Poznań province where I went on both social and political business the happy faces of girls with ribbon bows in their hair and the boys, their hair cut short leaving a fringe in an Indian style, continue to smile at me.

Those four and five year olds from primary schools, arguing among themselves as to who is to recite a poem at some festival or another! Every state celebration or church holy day is enthusiastically celebrated in Poland. Without the children's recitations no celebration is complete. And how they danced- the kujawiak, the krakowiak, the mazur, how they performed on the stage! I have not seen such a variety anywhere. Indeed, I have seen some who could rival film stars headed by Shirley Temple. The biggest problem was when children lost their milk teeth and the new ones had not yet appeared. Then, during the performance they would lisp. I shall never forget one five year old girl in a pleated little dress, four front teeth missing, reciting with a pronounced lisp a poem about *"Our Polish Sea"* – a sea she had never seen.

I met children in two primary schools where I was their doctor. I also looked after the children from the Healthcare Fund. I met them as a chairwoman of a women's organisation whose aim was to start a centre for Mothers & Children and was able to actively help those dear little patients of mine.

In the years 1930-1934 unemployment was very high in the district of Poznań where I lived. All organisations (and in that over-organised

Poznań province there were quite a number of them) went to the aid of the unemployed. But I considered myself the happiest of all when the superintendent of the Poznań Province Education Department gave approval to my organisation to distribute food to school children. How many of those children came to school without breakfast! Who knows better than I those pale little faces, those sad eyes of hungry children! I talked about this with the minister of Health & Social Care in Warsaw. As the result, the branch of Social Care for the Poznań province was granted extra funding from the ministry to supplement the food supply for children in Poznań. While on my visits to see the sick patients or on my return journey, I would drop in to a school where meals were served, and watch those youngsters stuff themselves with bread, soup and vegetables.

This is one of the few happy memories that remain with me from my stay in Poznań.

The doctor and the bailiff

In 1935 both my personal and business affairs were in a terrible state. Once the merger statute had been approved, the medical care contract for agricultural workers was cancelled. As a result I lost my income derived from it. On top of that the income from the Poznań Healthcare Fund was also reduced. As a GP I had to maintain a 5-room apartment, a telephone, and servants. The salary I received for my work was dependent on "annotation". Doctors received a fixed percentage of the annotated contributions based on a contract between the Medical Union and the Social Insurance. I think it worked out at around 13%-14% of the total income from the Healthcare Fund.

There were months when the collected contributions were low, or they were badly distributed. When that happened doctors received only a small payment. There was no such thing as a fixed, steady income. How was one to budget for everyday life in such circumstances? On top of that, the reduction of my income was so suddenly reduced by one third, that I was unable to adjust my standard of living based on this diminished scale, nor could I obtain additional work. I lived in an upmarket part of Poznań. This sudden drop in income meant I had to reduce that particular expenditure by 100%. I had to think of moving to a poorer district and renting no more than three rooms. But even the process of moving was a costly business!

At that point came the biggest nightmare of all – the tax office. Because doctors did not have steady employment, we paid taxes directly to the tax office. I paid income tax, turnover tax (turnover of what?), council tax which was 4% of total income, local tax and church tax.

The local council tax applied only in the territories formerly occupied by Prussia and was extremely burdensome. The tax on living accommodation was also excessively high, despite of the fact that landlords charged a low rent for well-appointed comfortable apartments. For instance for a five-room one the rent would be 150zł per month. Yet, the tax on it was based on the pre-war value of the apartment, which meant the tax payable was 40zl per month.[11]

Once the Poznań Province Healthcare Fund stopped their payments, my only income came from the Poznań Social Insurance. But even that income was severely reduced at source because the Medical Union took 4% of the gross amount. In addition there was also the so-called "Funeral Fund in Medical Chamber" paid by doctors at the rate of 40 zl. every second month. In cases of arrears bailiffs were called in.

With all those pressing mandatory obligations I twisted and turned like a snake in a thicket. And then I fell, crushed by the hammer of financial troubles when in 1935 the Treasury Department demanded payments dating back to 1930, which according to my records had been settled. I was informed that in 1931 I had paid only a 'limited' tax. The Treasure Department declined my appeal, and a 'full' tax was due for payment.

Where was the money to come from? I was not even able to cover my living expenses on my present salary. Once, unable to sleep, I got up very early and started to sort out various bills and statements – tax, official records, invoices, countless appeals and letters declining them. Those yellowing pieces of paper reminded me of the following frequent incidents.

Note 11: That makes it 27% on top of rent

I would return dead tired from my visits to patients, to be greeted by my son's nanny with the words: *'The bailiffs were here. They put seals on the dining room furniture and on your desk'*. This was my doctor's desk! I wasn't in any state to think about it. My time was taken up with visits to patients in the mornings, seeing more patients in the afternoon, meetings of the town council, and committee meetings of the various organisations which I chaired. It was my fault. I missed the settlement deadlines, but only some. It was enough to miss by just one day and there would be bailiffs the following day, scaring the living daylights out of my nanny and my son by putting seals on my furniture, leaving me with a reminder that I had neglected my duties.

But even King Solomon, it is said, cannot pour water from an empty jug. I had no money. I was due to receive some from the Social Insurance for outstanding fees, but the Medical Union had a claim on them. I didn't know how much was due to me, which meant I wasn't able to borrow against them to secure a loan, and pay the taxes.

The biggest wrong those tax offices did was to assume an income of 200zl per month from private patients. While I was looking after the Poznań poor, this in effect discouraged the *"better class"* ones. Who would be prepared to wait an hour in a doctor's waiting room sitting next to the ones like that worker from the tannery I had mentioned? The tax office demanded to see books to prove I had no private patients. What was I to do? Buy a book, and with its blank pages take it to the tax office? What was I to write in it if I had no private patients?

I remember very well the morning of 4 June 1935. Faced with a stack of tax demands in arrears and my utter, complete helplessness I felt faint. I just about managed to call my servant. She called one of my colleagues who used to take over from me on the few days when I had to leave Poznań to attend a meeting out of town. The Social Insurance did not automatically send in a locum in cases of illness or urgent business. For a doctor to take over you had to find one yourself and pay from your own pocket. Dr G. examined me and referred me to Professor J to admit me to hospital. My heart was not in a good state and it was impossible to treat me at home. I stayed for a month in a university clinic until my cardiac muscle recovered. I went back to work with my mind made up – I was going to leave Poznań.

A Polish village in the 1920s

My Warsaw Practice

Warsaw is my family home and I came back filled with renewed enthusiasm. My financial affairs had been settled as follows. The Poznań tax office auctioned off my better pieces of furniture and took all that was due to me from the Social Insurance. This meant that after thirteen years of employment I was left without any material means whatsoever. Fortunately what I had at my disposal were non-material ones. Several persons who knew of my work helped me to find employment with the Warsaw Social Insurance. Thus, for the third time in my life I set up a new GP practice.

As only two months elapsed between my working in Poznań and starting afresh in Warsaw, I am able to compare the difference between the two cities, details still fresh in my mind.

I was struck by two essential, and for me, important attitudes. First of all, I thought the administration in Warsaw was more clear-cut, worked better and more efficiently than in Poznań. Above all, the doctors' organisation - the Medical Union, dealt with me in a totally different way in terms of goodwill than in Poznań. I now think this subconscious hostility of the Poznań people stemmed from the fact I was not born in that part of Poland; I was not *"from there"*. Also there was, subconscious of course, an animosity between doctors themselves, reluctant to let in their younger colleagues to the practice given that patients had a free choice of GP. Put it this way – the Medical Union receives, let's say, 100,000zl. per month from the Social Insurance to be divided between, say, 200 doctors in the practice. Then, let us assume, fifty new doctors apply. But the income stays the same, so the Medical Union has to divide that 100,000zl. not between 200 doctors but 250. That meant that each doctor would now receive one fifth less than before. Although fully aware that young doctors needed to make a living, nevertheless they were not regarded as welcome.

This animosity, which I stress was subconscious, I did not notice among Warsaw doctors, where the attitude was completely different. When the Social Insurance wants to employ more doctors, they say- 'Great! There'll be more of us, so, at least theoretically, we can work not as hard.' In other words, there was no clash of interest, which to my mind is very important.

Also, taxes were deducted at source which made me very happy for not having to go to the tax office in person. I breathed a sigh of relief, but this was short-lived. My practice now was very different.

My patients

As I began my Warsaw practice I stuck on a smile on my face. I looked carefully into my patients' faces. I felt sure that by looking into their eyes I could detect what was ailing them having seen so much human suffering. The faces of patients coming to see me revolve in my mind as in a kaleidoscope. At first they were strangers – those people whose ailments and state of health I was about to discover.

The faces of my first patients were on the whole distrustful. It was rare for me to establish a good rapport. Some seemed insolent, others reserved, keeping a distance between us, speaking in tones either too pleading or too submissive. I will summarise my impressions at the end of this diary. Right now I will describe some of the more interesting cases. I will, of course, not supply names, honouring doctor/patient confidentiality.

A tender, sensitive nature

A woman came to see me, nicely dressed, rather plump, rosy complexion, 35, wife of a mechanic. It was obvious she took care of her appearance. She had lovely dark eyes, but their expression was somewhat dull. After my first, standard question "How can I help you?" an expression of suffering appeared in those dark eyes.

"It's my cough, I cough non-stop. I cannot sleep at nights,' she whispered, her lovely eyes filling with tears. 'I will not survive this, it's going to kill me."

"I am not sure I understand. What's going to kill you?"

"This dreadful cough."

"Well, let me see. Take off your top off please."

After examining her I found she was suffering from bronchitis. I prescribed several quick-acting medications and tried to calm her down.

"It's not very serious," I said. "The cough will soon pass," I told her gently.

"Perhaps, but that cough is making me deaf, my hearing is getting worse and worse."

I sent her to a specialist. She returned a week later, her lovely eyes brimming with distrust. She told me she still has a terrible cough and the ear medication did not help at all.

"I don't know how this will end. I am sure I have TB."

"But nobody in your family has TB. You are only thirty-five, you are not coughing up sputum, your temperature is normal, you look well, and the cough will definitely pass."

All the same, I sent her for a lung X-ray. A report came back with: *"Lungs show emphysematous changes. No fluid in the lungs."*

When she came to see me again I showed her the results of the X ray examination. I saw in her eyes distrust and contempt.

"Oh, that X ray examination. The moment I stood in front of that apparatus the doctor just glanced at it. Didn't take more than a minute. Well, what can you expect from the Social Insurance. You yourself said I had some kind of a lung disease," she added reproachfully.

"Yes, of course you are not well, but you don't have TB. You have bronchitis and suspected emphysema. But this will pass. We will continue with the medication," I continued patiently.

A few days later, another visit.

"I am terribly upset. I don't understand what is this emphysema. I am suffering from terrible headaches."

I examined her and noted there were no more crepitations in the lungs. I told her as gently as I could:

"I do understand you are in pain and suffering from headaches, but I hope you are no longer coughing."

The patient now satisfied that I believed her terrible sufferings, cheerfully agreed.

"Yes, true, I haven't been coughing since last week, but I still can't sleep at nights. Oh, doctor, could you explain to me what is this emphysema?"

There were about a dozen people in my waiting room getting impatient.

"I will explain some other time. Please trust me there is nothing seriously wrong with you. Come and see me next week."

After a week she returned in a raging mood.

"I have terrible headaches, it's as if somebody was hammering nails into my head."

I sent her to a neurologist and get a reply. *"Nothing neurological. Menopausal."*

That's a bit early for a menopause I thought to myself. I sent her to a gynaecologist who found out that she was pregnant. Ah, at last I understood. My patient was in a state of anxiety, she did not want the baby, but would say nothing about that, instead complaining of all kinds of ailments.

A month later she came to see me – this time all smiles. She told me she no longer coughs, her headaches gone. She felt she had to tell me everything that was bothering her, because going to a doctor was like going to a confession. She had an abortion and now feels weak. Indeed, my examination showed a weakening of the heart muscle. Looking after her now was getting easier because as she began to trust me, she took medication and injections regularly, and after about a month was well again. That was about a year and half ago.

Around three months later she came back, this time very polite, no shouts, no cries.

"Doctor, it's all come back. I know I am seriously ill again."

I didn't ask what ailed her, but taking advantage of the rapport we had built up with such difficulty, I asked:

"Do tell me what's happened. Anything wrong? What has upset you?'

'That dreadful crime."

I felt very uneasy.

"What crime?"

"I read about it in the papers - about a taxi driver who was killed and they took the taxi and drove away, and now I can't stop thinking about it. I know it will make me ill like I was those eighteen months ago."

"Why are you reading those tabloids if they upset you so much?"

"Because I don't want to sound ignorant. Everybody's talking about it right now. I don't want people to think I am not intelligent, so I read the papers regularly. I can't help the way it affects me, I am caring and sensitive, it's in my nature." As she spoke her eyes acquired a dreamy look.

And so the Social Insurance had to cover the cost of following the reports of sensational news, because a caring and sensitive patient of mine wanted to appear intelligent.

Liver disease

I sometimes observed cases when patients with serious heart conditions would not take prescribed medication, but would just lie there surrounded by bottles prescribed by various doctors, or ones suffering from liver disease who did not believe the medicines would help and so simply poured out the contents.

It was therefore a pleasant surprise when a lady came to see me and thanked me for having cured her. She had been suffering from a liver problem, but by taking what I had prescribed and sticking to a diet of broths and soups, her health had improved and her symptoms had resolved. She was fifty years old, wife of a type-setter, always well dressed. She would come with a novel to read while waiting to see me.

I felt very happy. Normally patients would come with a long list of complaints. I knew I should keep a degree of equanimity, yet I couldn't

71

help feeling pleased. I felt I should say something complimentary in return. "It's a pleasure to see someone who is sensible and understands I am here to advise the best I can. I am glad to see you are better. There was another lady here with the same complaint who told me she was not going to take the medicine I prescribed because it tasted bitter."

While I was talking the face of my patient reflected satisfaction, even pride. She said:

"Ah, don't bother with the likes of them. Just give them half a litre of vodka and half a kilo of krakowska sausage."

"But that wouldn't do their liver any good," I objected. "Besides, the Social Insurance would not be able to afford such prescriptions."

On the other hand, who knows? Perhaps it would make some of the patients happy and perhaps they would finally stop complaining about the Healthcare Fund.

Syphilis

It began with an argument. A very handsome man, tall, dark hair, came with a brown insurance card which showed he did not live in my catchment area.

"You should have gone to your GP."

"You are my GP."

"The street where you live is not covered by my practice."

"That's where I used to live. I've since moved to your area."

"All right," I said, "You can consult with me this one time, but next time please bring the correct document with you."

The man was very cross.

"This is intolerable. I need to be seen by a doctor and what I get is a load of formalities."

"I can't help it. I cannot look after people who are not in my catchment area. I have a great number of patients who come to see me as it is. You yourself have been waiting here for an hour. Still, since you are here, I'll examine you. Where does it hurt?"

I looked at his pale face expressing fatigue and resentment, and at his yellowing hands.

"I don't know what's wrong. I feel weak," he said.

"Have you been ill lately?"

"Not particularly."

Having examined him it was clear he had an inflamed aorta. I looked carefully at him.

"When did you contract syphilis?" I asked him steadily.

He looked shocked.

"You are ill, you need to be treated. I am asking you whether you had treatment for it, and if you had a blood test done."

The man, still in a state of shock, began to talk. He had contracted syphilis ten years ago but did not treat it for six years. He then went through six syphilis treatments. The blood analysis for the Wasserman reaction came back negative, the examination of the spinal fluid was apparently positive.

"Why didn't you tell me about it straight away? I might have missed vasculitis of the aorta; I might have thought that you are only feeling unwell or that your heart muscle has been weakened by something else."

I gave him medication for the heart and sent him to a venereologist.

Next time he brought with him the correct papers, so I had no doubt he did live in my area. He was in a better mood, telling me he now understands there are rules to check where one lives and works. I suspected he had lodged a complaint and was given an explanation.

"Are you feeling better?" I asked.

"Yes, I sleep better now. Could you prescribe me some drops I can carry with me?"

"Why?"

"Because I am in constant fear I might trip and fall any moment. I am afraid to go out and meet people, I am scared I might faint and collapse in somebody's presence."

"I don't see any reason why you should feel anxious," I said. "You have a weak heart that's true, and it's a pity you had not been treated in those six years. However, with treatment that can be dealt with. But why should you be afraid of meeting people? Surely being on your own won't do you any good."

The patient in reply spoke, as if to himself.

"I'll be in the theatre with someone and then I'll trip and fall."

I knew he was an educated man, a university graduate, working in some office. I decided to confront him.

73

"Are you afraid of dying?" I asked.

"I am not afraid of death, only of being a burden to a person I am with when I lose consciousness and fall."

"But this is irrelevant," I tried to cheer him up. "You really needn't worry what people think if you are faced with a terminal illness or death. However, right now there is no question of this being a terminal illness or you dying. Here is a prescription for reviving drops in case you feel faint. Do take your lady friend (it's really easy to be clairvoyant) to the theatre. There is no point in leading a dull life. You need your sleep, you need to rest after work and after dinner, but there is no reason to stay away from people. Nobody has to know what happened to you ten years ago unless you yourself tell them - that will remain between you and your doctors. Just continue with your treatment. Marriage right now is out of the question."

He left. His symptoms of weakness of the cardiac muscle improved quickly. After a month he stopped coming to see me, but for the next six months continued to see the venereologist.

Then he came again shaken and distressed to ask for a sick leave note. He was ill for three days and did not go to work.

"But Social Insurance does not issue those notes, and anyway, I have not seen you in those three days."

"I have been going through a dreadful time. My personal life is in ruins. I cannot have children."

"Who told you that?"

"The venereal specialist."

I wrote out a certificate on my private form stating I had been treating him for a heart condition. He left in a calmer state of mind. When and in what state will I see him again? I was much moved by his bleak prospects and despair. Why didn't he start his treatment earlier?

Dear patients – do not shy away from the treatment of syphilis.

A Lady with influence

Normally I see my patients in the mornings between 9 and 10, then I leave the house. One day when I got back home around two pm for my afternoon surgery, my servant said to me:

"There was a lady here, called around midday, one of the better class ones. She wanted to be seen immediately, and said that if you won't go and see her this very minute, she'll make such a scene the like of which you'll never forget."

"So what did you do, you poor thing, seeing as I wasn't in?" I asked laughing.

"I swore you weren't in. She said I was lying. Then she gave me her membership card and told me you are to go and see her the moment you come back."

I looked at the membership card and could not believe my eyes. It belonged to a clerk employed by one of our top banks. Obviously, my servant must have got something wrong. I decided to go and see this "polite" sick lady for myself.

The woman, twenty-eight years old, was lying in bed, her face wrapped in flannel. She told me she had a toothache. Both the bedside table and the bed were covered by various medicines prescribed by a private doctor, of course. She gave me a withering look, her unfriendly eyes sizing me up and down before finally opening her mouth accompanied by a regal wave of the hand.

"I don't need anything from you other than a note stating I can't go to the office because I am seriously ill. I am being treated by a private doctor," she said pointing to the medicines.

"I need to examine you in order for me to issue you with a sick leave note," I told her. "I must say I am surprised. You could have called during my surgery hours since you're quite obviously not housebound."

"I was coming back from the dentist, so I dropped in on the way back, but you weren't in - of course. Right now I am feeling seriously unwell and in no state to go out again," my "sick" patient replied.

I examined her. Apart from generally not looking well, and a slight weakness of the cardiac muscle most likely temporary, I could not find anything wrong. Her temperature was normal.

"Why did you request a visit? If you were able to see a dentist you could've also managed to see a doctor. I'd also like to say that the way you spoke to my servant today was inappropriate. I am surprised a person like you, employed by a respectable institution, would behave like that."

"I am not going to talk about it any more," my "refined" patient

75

replied. "As far as I'm concerned I've no confidence in you, none whatsoever. Anyway, I have the ear of some important people."

I sent the patient to the department dealing with applications for the leave of absence. A month later one of my colleagues told me a complaint has been lodged against me.

"What complaint?" I asked much surprised. "All my patients seem to be doing all right, nobody's died, there are no complications, even two old ladies who I expected to be in their grave are still on their feet and walking. So, what could that complaint be about?"

"Apparently you are brutal and abrupt. You do not listen to your patients. Patients are reluctant to come and see you and do so only if they absolutely must."

Now this was a devastating accusation. I felt it could only have come from the 'lady with influence'. I am not sure if that complaint was ever made, because officially I have not heard anything more about it.

A secretary to the minister

Power goes to some people's heads. I think women are perhaps more prone to fall into its grip. One evening, just before the practice closing time I heard shouts and commotion in the corridor. Six people still waiting to be seen were protesting loudly. Someone wanted to skip the queue. Unable to carry on with my consultation with that racket going on, I went out to see what was happening. In the corridor I found an elderly lady who introduced herself, but not by name.

"I am a secretary to minister X. I'm sending my servant to your practice."

I understood this to mean the servant was in need of urgent attention.

"Where is this girl?" I asked.

"I will send her immediately."

I am thinking it's nearly 6 pm, consultations are coming to an end, and she only intends to send her in. I say nothing, because faced with powers from above it is better to keep one's mouth shut. I did the right thing. The minister's secretary did not live in my district. Thank heavens! She must have realised her mistake because she sent her servant to another doctor.

I heard my colleagues had a lot of trouble with this madam secretary, but as this is circumstantial I will not say any more.

Two men with duodenal ulcer

I'm a little apprehensive to continue writing having read what I have written in the last two chapters, in order not to remind myself of turbulent emotions resulting from tactlessness when dealing with various ladies "with influence".

Instead I'll write about two patients of mine who I remember with a degree of satisfaction. They were a driver and a cook – I don't remember them because they were very polite when they came to see me, they weren't and probably cursed me behind my back, but because after two years of my treatment they both made a good recovery.

I'll write about the two of them together because I diagnosed their problem with the help of X rays, applied similar treatment, and noted their recovery, all roughly at the same time. There was one significant difference – the driver was satisfied and happy; the cook continued to curse all doctors, hospitals, the Insurance and the intelligentsia in general, to kingdom come. Apart from that, everything else followed a similar pattern so that I can put them together in one chapter. Their income was roughly the same, and both were fathers of several children.

The driver was one of my first patients in Warsaw. He came to see me at the surgery, I don't know why, because he was in a very poor state and he was perfectly justified to ask for a home visit. He suffered from bleeding duodenal ulcers, was generally in poor shape, pale, his pulse weak. I made him rest in my consulting room for half an hour before letting him go home. But he improved after less than two months of treatment. I looked up my short notes: *"16.1.1936 – slight burning sensation after meals". "22.1.1936 – no heartburn". "30.1.1936 – patient feeling better".* From that time on he came for his medication once every two months, took the prescribed mixtures of various salts, and was compliant with treatment. After a couple of years I thought his weight had increased by 50% and he was looking hale and hearty compared with when I first met him.

The cook suffered from the same problem. He admitted that he felt better when he followed my advice and diet. But he found it difficult to stick to the diet given his job, and then his health deteriorated plunging him into despair. He would then curse everyone and everything.

When I asked him why he did not stick to the diet? He told me curtly: "What do I need that diet for? That's for other people. I cook my own meals and I make sure they're good and wholesome. What harm is there in a good steak fried in fresh butter?"

I found it difficult to argue with that kind of argument, especially as the patient was convinced that if he prepared the food himself it would not do him any harm.

I also had two similar cases, two cooks from first rate restaurants suffering from stomach and duodenal ulcers. What would the stomachs of clients of those restaurants be like, if the creators of that cuisine were not doing well themselves?

The only cure for a painful toe is to cut the leg off

That's what one patient said to me. The poor man suffered from arthritis, unfortunately combined with neurasthenia. In my opinion even the worst conditions can improve dramatically if a person has patience and confidence in his doctor, the two creating a battle front. The sick person believes he will get better and what else could a doctor wish for if not to cure him. Thus, together, they are ready for battle, almost like going to war. If this attitude is supported by reasonable living conditions, good nursing, and goodwill of relatives and friends then, as long as it's not cancer or last stages of TB, both emerge victorious.

My patient, unfortunately, showed no inclination to join the battle with me. He was constantly angry. He complained endlessly about the Social Insurance. Whenever I saw him I could not help but wonder why sick people, particularly in Warsaw, were so demanding. In the provinces the attitude towards doctors and the Social Insurance was more, how shall I put it, considerate. Perhaps it was because there was more poverty and unemployment there. Poorer people were more appreciative of the advantages offered by Social Insurance than those who had always been well off, who enjoyed a reasonable standard of living and could afford private treatment if necessary. If he belonged to the latter there was no reason not to complain about Social Insurance. Whenever I came across a malcontent reciting the usual list of complaints I would interrupt with questions:

"Are you really so hard done by? What harm has Social Insurance done you? Have you been denied treatment by a doctor? Didn't Social Insurance pay your benefits? Were you ever refused a hospital treatment?"

That would usually silence the malcontents. I tried my best to calm them down, listen to their various grievances and make things easier for them. And so it was in this case.

My patient suffering from arthritis and acutely painful toe of the left foot once suggested I give him a note for a treatment in a sanatorium.

"What do you need it for?" I asked. "You need to be examined by a medical commission first in order to claim the costs from Social Insurance."

"I know that, I need it only for my employer. I'll cover all the costs myself, because no medication from the Insurance is any good anyway."

I produced the required note. Two months later I was called to see the principal director. I had to explain why I did not act according to the rules, why I did not send the patient to be seen by the medical commission before he applied for the costs of treatment in the sanatorium.

I realised the patient had deceived me. I made a promise to myself never to comply with patients' requests that were not in line with the rules. Shortly afterwards I was proved right in my resolution. Two months later the same patient came to see me, this time demanding to have his leg amputated because the pain in his toe was unbearable. I decided not to comply with his request, instead prescribing him an anti-arthritic treatment, and referred him to a neurologist. Thankfully he is still walking on both legs, and no longer insists on amputation.

Based on an example of this case I concluded never to give in to patients' demands, even when they feel hard done by the Social Insurance, because left to themselves they might push the rules too far.

"Seriously ill"

I took in the appearance and details of my "seriously ill" patient. Manicure, pedicure, hair permed and bleached, eyebrows charcoal black. Husband a locksmith, expected to support a wife who does nothing but lounge all day on the sofa. No question of children.

This resident of Warsaw suburbs was an hour and a half late for her appointment.

"Oh, doctor not in? Well then, in this case I must ask her to take the trouble and visit me at home,'" she said to my servant leaving her membership card.

I went. My patient opened the door herself.

"I couldn't stay in bed any longer," she said. "I've been waiting for you these last four hours."

I entered the bedroom where I found the husband of my sick patient in bed.

"How can I help? What's wrong?"

"I feel poorly."

I examined her carefully and found nothing wrong. Absolutely nothing at all.

"One more trick like this and I will report you to the authorities and you will have to pay a fine," I told her.

A month later, half hour after closing time the door bell began to ring continuously. The servant would not let any more patients in explaining: "The doctor has four more patients to see and surgery hours have already finished."

The lady refused to leave, ignored the servant's explanation, and continued to press the bell. Finally I had to go outside to see what was going on. There stood the same "charming" wife of the locksmith. I told the servant to let her in and to wait at the end of the queue. As she entered, her face all innocence, the other women in the waiting room raised their voices the moment they saw her. When one of them came into my consulting room she spoke at once:

"Why did you let her in? We know her only too well. She's our neighbour. Her brother is a policeman, that's why she acts so la-di-da. Always complaining, got our caretaker into trouble and our shopkeeper too. She's nothing but trouble. Pox on her!"

At last it was the turn of this suburban beauty to come in. She wore an angelic expression, one could almost see white wings emerging from her back.

"How can I help you?" I asked.

"I am seriously ill. I cannot sleep at nights. I should've asked you

80

to visit me, only I could not find anyone to send in. I've asked the caretaker, I've asked the neighbours, no one was there to help me."

I examined my "seriously ill" patient again. What should I prescribe, I was thinking to myself, a bromide or a penalty for taking advantage of the Social Insurance. Oh, if only I could prescribe a stay in some working camp for women! That would've been the best medicine. Not only for her, but for other suburban "ladies of leisure" - the very best of medicines – work!

Cancer

As I write this word I am reminded of all my patients who died of it, their terrible suffering and that dreadful process of dying. The pain in this world is not an empty word for a doctor fighting for the life of her patients and her helplessness as it rebounds on her. How many patients have I seen suffering from it! In Warsaw this dreadful disease is much more frequent than in the country. I am not sure about the statistics, but I saw 50% more cases in Warsaw.

From the many cases I saw I will describe one, which I would like to dedicate to a nurse of the Warsaw branch of the Social Insurance, Mrs R. the epitome of dedication, tact and kindness.

In 1936 a very pleasant, attractive lady came to see me. Carefully permed grey hair contrasted with her youthful complexion. Deeply set beautiful eyes. Used to work at the Ministry of Education. She came from the Eastern part of Poland and spoke in the soft accents of those parts. A dignified, strictly regulated, orderly conduct was her rule in life. During her visit she discretely drew my attention to the lighting on my desk which she considered incorrect. While she talked politely and pleasantly I kept quiet and listened carefully.

Five years ago she was diagnosed with breast cancer. Her left breast was removed, followed by many sessions of radiotherapy. She no longer worked, was receiving a pension and now had registered with the Social Insurance, having spent all her savings on private treatments. She was forty-eight.

"My joints are very painful,' she complained. 'You cannot imagine what torture it is to get up, wash, dress and comb my hair. I am very particular when it comes to personal hygiene; I wash myself from head to foot every day. Right now I find it difficult even to put my feet on

81

the floor when I get out of bed."

"Can't somebody help you?" I asked.

"No, I live alone. I have a bachelor flat on the fifth floor, not far from here. And what agony it is to tidy up my room," she added, as an afterthought.

I examined her and was horrified to find hard lymphatic nodes under her armpit. So, it's cancer all right. Even though several years had gone after the removal of the breast, the cancer still did not let go of its victim and has moved to her right breast. Of course, I did not want to tell my patient that, and instead I put on a happy face.[12]

"This is not something I can deal with here. You should be treated in hospital."

I emphasised that she lived on her own and didn't have any help. I was certainly not going to let on that there was nothing I could do for her that as a physician; only a surgeon and a radiologist could be of help.

She continued to delay further referral. She was always very charming and for a long time very politely, but firmly refused to go to the hospital.

"Even though it is difficult for me to climb up the five flights of stairs I prefer to come to see you here. I am sure you have many sick patients to visit, so I won't trouble you to visit me," she said.

Oh, if only those ladies – "grand", "influential", "beautiful" threatening me with complaints while they were "fainting" in their dirty beds, could hear!

I told her it was my duty to visit seriously ill patients. I could visit her even without a visit request and assured her she could always call me whenever she felt worse. All this time I continued to press her to go to the hospital.

She did have friends in various places and finally went for treatment at a university clinic under the care of one of the professors there, her costs covered by the Social Insurance. They started her on a course of radiotherapy, about forty in all. But she did not stay long at the clinic, she was not happy there, and her health did not improve; on

Note 12: It was common practise not to mention the word 'Cancer' right up to recent times.

the contrary it was getting progressively worse. Already under a death sentence she was sent home where her martyrdom began. How this sentence contrasted with her appearance! Always very elegantly dressed, cheeks carefully made up, she told me the hospital doctors seeing her rosy cheeks could not believe she was seriously ill. It showed that even in that shred of life left to her she was not going to be pushed down, and fought for her appearance to the very end.

How tragic that was, as I believe she had no other aim in life other than striving for perfection of body and soul. She lived alone, in that bachelor flat on the fifth floor, not married, not in touch with her family. She blamed rheumatism for the muscle pains characteristic of cancer. Apart from the appropriate medication, I had to prescribe various ointments she believed would help. I wanted to maintain the illusion that things will improve so I continued to give her injections of restorative tonic, in the forlorn hope that *"maybe it'll work"*.

These injections required daily visits from a nurse from the Social Insurance. I knew Mrs R. as a first-rate nurse, but I didn't know then of her selflessness and devotion to patients. Mrs R. had her hands full because at the time there was a flu epidemic in Warsaw. Nurses were needed to administer the cupping therapy and injections. Mrs R. was seeing seventeen to eighteen patients a day, yet she always found time to stay and chat for this patient suffering from cancer. She was so kind and gentle that this lady who was always ready to criticise and complain about other nurses, came to trust her.

The cancer continued to progress, the pains became stronger, and the medication I prescribed to reduce them failed to work. I had to resort to morphine, at first in powder form. The dose had to be steadily increased because her dreadful pains were such she could not sleep and would scream all night long. She lived, as I mentioned, in a bachelor flat, and her neighbours, mostly professionals, complained that her screams were so disturbing that they themselves could not sleep either. In spite of this, they were very considerate and tried to help, although as each week passed she became more and more bad-tempered.

The cancer not only invaded her right breast but also appeared on her scalp. I begged her to go to the hospital. She would not hear about it, saying "I'll never get a better treatment than I am getting now."

"But you are on your own, alone all day, totally dependent on others to help you get dressed and prepare a meal."

"I have all I need by the bed," she would say.

True, she managed to organise things so that both food and toiletries were to hand. Either a neighbour or a member of the family brought meals every day, so things were not too bad.

In spite of the seriousness of the illness, she continued to take care of her appearance. Once in great confidence she decided to teach me how to make the cheeks look rosy, and even demonstrated how to do it. She rubbed a lipstick on a piece of cotton wool and gently rubbed it on the cheeks. How pitiful all this was. In order to cheer her up I said:

"A lipstick will not help those with rough and blotchy skin. It works so well on you because yours is smooth and soft."

She was very pleased to hear that. My remark was followed by further confidences. It turned out that she had once been beautiful and had many admirers. She led a disciplined life, spent a lot of time doing gymnastics and hydrotherapy. People called her a lover of nature; she loved long walks, followed a strict regime, always going to bed at nine and getting up at six, and never wavered from it. This was a woman whom cancer caught in its talons!

I could not devote more than forty minutes per visit because at that time I had my hands full dealing with the flu epidemic, rampant in Warsaw in 1937. I could only visit her once a week. Besides, how could I help her? There was no longer any point in operating because the cancer had spread practically everywhere, so that she was showing symptoms of cancer poisoning, the so called 'cachexia'. The surgeon could not do anything either and limited his help to an occasional visit.

The nurse, however, visited her every day. To stay with her and listen to her talk usually took over an hour. Mrs R. often finished her work around eleven in the evening. She would leave the visit to her last, so that there was no need to hurry to other patients and leave the impression that the lady was one of a thousand she was looking after. Often Mrs R. unable to finish her rounds earlier would call when the main gates were already locked for the night. My sick lady would be waiting for her patiently.

I felt this was taking unfair advantage of Mrs R. and requested a full time carer. A private nurse was found, but my patient insisted only Mrs R. could give her the injections I prescribed. Her pains by that time were so intense I had to resort to opiates. Normally a dose worked for ten days, but had to be increased as time went on. When the medicines ran out, the private nurse would come to me to get a fresh prescription and tell me all kinds of stories about the sick woman. According to her she was a monster of the worst kind, treated her abominably, and would not allow her to touch anything.

The stories Mrs R. told me were just the opposite. She considered the sick lady to be full of good will. When I told her there was no need for her to administer the enema, the private nurse could do that, she explained: "I do it after hours, and she is sensitive and difficult to please. She believes if her intestines function well and she can eat, everything will turn out all right."

This went on for three months, three months of excruciating pain and slow death. The cancer was progressing slowly but surely. The morphine did its best. By this time not a day passed without an injection. It was as if a black vulture spread its wings over that poor human body.

On one of my visits my patient said to me: "There's one more thing I'd like to do in my life – to rent a horse cab and go with you to the Łazienki park[13] for a long drive. But I suppose someone would have to carry me back to the fifth floor."

Shortly after this conversation she developed paralysis followed by ileus of the alimentary canal. She could no longer eat nor pass a bowel motion.

Usually at five in the afternoon Mrs R. would come for further instructions regarding the patients I had seen that day. One day I received a telephone call from Mrs R. very much upset.

"That patient on the fifth floor, what's going to happen to her?"

"What do you mean? Don't you know what happens to people with cancer?"

"Yes, I do, I understand now," she said in a voice full of grief.

When I saw the sick woman for the last time, the day before she died, she was slipping in and out of consciousness which was a blessing

Note 13: A lovely park in Warsaw

for her. I could tell she recognised me, because the corners of her mouth lifted in a smile and she whispered something. I could only understand one word – 'doctor'. I stroked her tussled hair, smiled and said:

"You will be well at last. No more pain."

I truly believed that it was impossible for her to suffer any more. I felt a lump in my throat; I could stay no longer. I stroked her hair again and shook her hand. By the time I had walked down the five flights of stairs both my handkerchiefs were wet. When I got home I took a big dose of bromide. Between 4-6 pm there will be patients waiting to see me. I had to appear calm and collected. I opened my consulting room on time.

"Who is next, please?"

Some socio-literary reflections and about five drinkers

I was able to look up some statistics and compare the official figures with my *"sociological experiences"*. This was an opportunity to compare the two, but I don't want to compare them, I want to write as I see and feel, and maybe they will be reconciled of their own accord.

The way I see it people in the country drink relatively less than those living in towns and cities. As to alcoholism, the biggest concentration is in the capital. It's very simple. If a drinker drinks away all his money, but is surrounded by a convivial company, they will continue to buy drinks for him. In the country such an arrangement does not exist – where will a drinker find the money to buy vodka? But an office worker, a teacher, a farmer arriving at the capital will want to have some fun. The inhabitants of Warsaw are well known as a merry lot. Especially those who frequent bars. They lie in wait for some provincial fool who stands the rounds while showing off his parochial ignorance.

Drinkers form a sort of brotherhood. A man slightly less drunk will take care of one who is more drunk acting as a sort of nanny. And how pleasantly they converse when they meet again at a *"dinner"* in the bar *"Grand"*, from which they move on to the first, second, third *"tea"* at other bars. Oh, the pits of human soul! How little and how rarely come those who could light up those psychological dens into which young people fall. What devastation alcohol brings to our clever, professional

86

class! Drunkenness has its place in literature; I need add nothing to Lewis Sinclair who wrote about the conscience of America. But that's not what I wish to discuss.

As a doctor I had to take a stand when faced with incidents of drunkenness which, unfortunately, I came across frequently, and not limited to the *"bottom of society"* either.

During the last winter an exceptional number of people came to my consulting room. It was the season of 'flu, angina, pneumonia. At one point I heard loud noises in my waiting room. I went out to see what was going on. I looked carefully at the people in the waiting room, scanning the familiar faces until I found the source of the noise. It was a man with thick, grey hair. I thought he must be one of those who habitually complained about the Social Insurance. I smiled at everybody and closed the door. I particularly mention the smile, because I consider a friendly smile creates a good relationship between the sick person and myself. I am conscious of the fact I might be dealing with patients who have bad tempered bosses at work, or complaints in the family, or money problems generally. All this creates an unfriendly aura for a sick person. For one who is well and strong a bad atmosphere around him does no harm, while the nervous system of the sick only gets worse. That is why I am always friendly towards them even though I might be tired, or not feeling well, or troubled myself when the smile might not be spontaneous but a result of force of will. I sometimes feel I am a walk on part in a drama. Nevertheless my working life forces me to reach out to a sick person and find an instant solution to certain problems and so my most frequent reaction is to smile. I am afraid I am copying Proust at this moment, so am going back to the stories of my patients.

When the turn came to see the impatient, noisy man I learnt he was a writer of some renown. He came in order for me to sign a note issued by a rehabilitation clinic. Somehow I managed to pacify him. He consulted me again, more than ten times, even gave me one of his books, very beautiful, with his dedication.

When I read it I asked him whether alcohol had an influence on his writing. He told me that at the beginning of his *"alcoholic career"* he managed to get an idea which he might not have had if he didn't drink.

But creating the whole concept of the work, giving it a shape must be done in full consciousness that is, with a clear head. By the time I met him, he was unable to create anything.

He was being treated most assiduously in the clinic. My role was limited to issuing prescriptions they were prescribing. Finally I suggested I could contact an institution where he could be treated. I got in touch with a neurologist and was told the depressing news that although institutions for nervous disorders which treat alcoholism do exist, they give no guarantees, because an alcoholic will always find a way to smuggle vodka in.

I strongly recommended my patient to the neurologist, but he did not contact him. Alcoholics, it seems, love their vodka so much they avoid anyone who tries to discourage them from drinking.

*

The family life of an alcoholic is one big mess. Wives of alcoholics would come to me wailing about it, the same of which could not be said about the alcoholics themselves. They did not complain. I had one pleasant lady patient with menopausal problems. She felt well, and was about to come to the end of her treatment. In one of her last visits she told me her life story.

"I once had a dog, lovely, little dog, I loved it. We have no children as you know, and this dog was my single joy. Oh, I have its photograph here…'"

She showed me a photograph of herself on a street with an indifferent-looking mongrel on a lead.

"The dog got lost,' she continued. 'I put up notices, I searched for him everywhere. I never found him. Now I think I'll go mad with this drunkard at home."

"So, your husband drinks?" I asked.

The woman got very agitated.

"He doesn't just drink, he guzzles it. As soon as he comes back from work he orders me to bring him a quarter[14] which he drinks every evening and then falls asleep. If there is no vodka in the house when he wakes up at 2 or 3 in the morning, I have to go out and buy some, or he'll start breaking the furniture. "You idiot", I tell him, "You'll end

Note 14: Quarter of a litre

up in a pit." When I say this he goes for me and beats me. I'm scared of him. Once he hit me very badly."

The woman was crying. What to advise, what to say to her?

"I can prescribe something that causes an aversion to vodka. Those who took it now avoid alcohol altogether. Do you think you could manage to make him take it?"

"If it's just medicine he won't take it."

"Maybe you can mix it with food?"

"He eats very little. He just drinks vodka and I can't put anything in the drink because he'll be able to tell."

"How do you yourself manage, have you enough for the rent and food?" I asked.

"My husband used to earn good money as a locksmith at the power station, but they chucked him out on account of his drinking. Now he works at a private firm. He gives me all the money he earns so I can't complain but it's on condition that I'll buy the vodka for him. That's how I manage to make ends meet, because if you don't drink it in the bar it's not that expensive."

"Seeing as you managed to get your husband not go to bars and spend his money there, maybe you can give him that medicine in a liquid form."

The woman took the prescription gratefully and repeated it three times before coming back again.

"My husband says he'll kill me if I don't stop putting this garbage into his vodka. He told me last week it lost all its taste for him, now it tastes like grass."

On reflection, it seemed to me, this problem cannot be resolved by chemistry. It would be just too good if a mixture of bromide, chlorohydrate and belladonna was to resolve the problem of weak will and psychological disturbance. I am not a psychiatrist and this is not part of my practice. But as a GP I must deal with all the pathological cases I come across in my consulting room.

*

Having examined a man working in a power station, I found an infection of kidneys, degeneration of the heart muscle and an enlarged liver.

"How much vodka do you drink a day?" I asked.

89

The man was indignant.

"Just because I am a working man, you think I am an alcoholic?"

"Dear Sir," I said patiently, "I am a doctor, I have just examined you and my results show symptoms associated with alcoholism. That's why I asked you. I want to help you. Besides, vodka is drunk even more by the so-called intelligentsia. Among the workers only the better paid drink a lot and you can count them on the fingers of your hand."

The man was somewhat pacified and admitted he did drink vodka. He promised to cut down. But I have serious doubts that he kept his promise.

*

I was also looking after a cook working on the railway, a printer, and an evening classes lecturer. I noticed a marked similarity among them, even though they had no idea of each other's existence. They were all between thirty and fifty years old, thin, fidgety, in conversation excitable and cheerful. Their confidence melted like ice under the sun when they were compelled to do something that they did not want to do. Then they became shy and submissive.

As patients they were extraordinarily polite and listened very carefully to my advice. But I have my doubts that they carried out any of it once they got home.

Social Insurance – an object of dislike

The dislike of the Social Insurance was extraordinarily widespread in Warsaw. Its manifestations hit me like a cudgel on the head from the time I left Poznań and began to practice in Warsaw. Here are some examples (I'll summarise them later).

On my fifth day of consulting in Warsaw practice an athletic looking man came to see me. While still in the doorway of my consulting room he began to talk in a loud voice.

"I pay my subscription only to be met with a bloody racket. You were supposed to send a hospital nurse to do the cupping, we've been waiting for three hours and nobody came. Is that your attitude to a working man, is that how you treat the working class? I don't want to put anybody's nose out of joint, I've no wish to be rude, all I am saying it's a flipping outrage and a scandal."

I was shaken to the core. I said nothing, it was not prudent to interrupt an enraged man's flow of words, but I was deeply offended by being accused of treating workers badly. Oh, if only my friend and colleague with whom I worked in a workers' organisation had heard that! He'd have told this man a thing or two. This accusation had momentarily shaken my self-assurance. However, I did manage to listen attentively to the man while he talked. When he finally stopped I took over.

"As far as I am concerned you've been extremely rude. I don't know you and see no reason why you came here. Let me see your membership card."

It turned out the sick woman on whose account this voluble man came to see me was not in my area and it was not up to me to send a hospital nurse. A misunderstanding, but a big shock to my nervous system.

*

A telephone call: "Oh doctor, I am your neighbour, I live not far from your place. My wife is not feeling well," I am told in "genteel" tones.

I went to visit the sick woman. A servant opened the door.

"Oh, mistress is having a bath. Please wait."

"I don't have much time. I have other patients waiting for me. Please tell your mistress I'll not be able to stay long," I said.

After ten minutes I finally saw the patient. As I suspected, she was all charm, looking delightful in a lace-trimmed night dress. Her lovely eyes, in spite of her thirty-three years were like that of a doe, a wounded doe of course. I could imagine she used the same sad expression when asking her husband to buy her a new hat.

"Oh," she sighed, a long, exhausted sigh. "So my husband did ring for you. I feel absolutely dreadful. I am running a high temperature."

I took her temperature, it was 37.3 ^{0}C. I examined her thoroughly. Apart from a slight reddening in the throat, I found nothing wrong. I prescribed medicine for the throat, and sent a nurse to give her an anti-flu injection, thinking that would be the end of that.

In fact, it was only the beginning. She consulted again, saying that her temperature is normal, but it goes up once she gets up and starts to walk around.

91

It's possible, I thought to myself, I'll do an analysis, maybe there is an infection somewhere. I had just got home when I received a phone call from her husband, asking for a nurse because his wife bought an injection and needed a nurse to administer it. My reply was curt.

"I will not be sending a nurse because there is no need for another injection. She is due for an X ray examination, she is to have a urine analysis and to make an appointment with a throat specialist."

She came to see me the moment I returned after my month's holiday.

"I saw the Social Insurance throat specialist," she said. "He was not polite, only looked at my throat and gave me a gargle. Naturally I went to see a doctor privately, perhaps you know him, Dr. P. " she added, looking at me triumphantly. I caught her tone immediately.

"I can imagine the result!" I exclaimed.

The woman, undeterred, continued:

"….'And who was looking after you?' asked the doctor. 'Who, if not the Social Insurance?' I said to him. 'Well, well', said the private doctor. 'This is a sorry state of affairs. You have suppurative tonsillitis. I am prescribing 15 diathermy treatments for the throat, and a gargle'. So I've come to ask you to prescribe for me the same medication the private doctor has prescribed."

I looked at the prescription. The medication was almost identical to the one I described six weeks ago.

"I will prescribe the gargle on the Social Insurance form. As to the other treatment you should see a laryngologist, I am not a specialist." I said.

"Oh, but you have to wait there for such a long time to see one. Could you please prescribe it for me now?" she pressed on.

I repeated what I have just said, and gave her the prescription for the gargle. When I handed it to her she repeated four times the demand for the diathermy treatment, and each time I refused.

"I am not a laryngologist and I cannot take the responsibility for something I have not prescribed."

The patient was very upset.

Next day she sent in her servant girl who tried to skip the queue. People in the waiting room loudly objected. When eventually she came into my consulting room, I asked her for her membership card not

92

knowing what had gone on before. The girl said she'd been sent by Mrs Y. to collect a prescription for a cough syrup. She had no membership card with her and said the syrup was what owed from Mrs Y's visit yesterday, only she forgot to mention it while she was here.

I said I have no idea what syrup she is talking about and told the girl to tell her mistress to come and see me in person when she feels unwell, and not send a domestic servant, and also she should not expect a GP to prescribe medication by being told what to prescribe.

"Am I to tell her that?" asked the girl.

"Yes, please do."

Two days later Mrs Y. asked for a visit. This is the time, I thought to myself, to cut the Gordian's knot. Before leaving I checked her records. Analyses and the X ray showed a slightly raised temperature which could be due to an inflammation of the tonsils, but no problems with the heart, lungs, kidneys or liver. I went to see her equipped with all possible instruments. I found the patient feeling ill and in bed. She has high temperature, she told me. I checked. It was 37.1^0C. I could see tonsillar exudate. I asked her if she went to see the specialist.

"I go for the diathermy privately. I am fed up with the Social Insurance. And I don't see why I cannot send my servant to fetch the prescription for me when I am not feeling well. The private doctor I was seeing always gave it to her."

I felt I had to set the record straight.

"Please do not send your domestic servant to me for prescriptions unless I specifically say so. I see you are dissatisfied with the Social Insurance yet you continue to use it in an inappropriate way. I cannot prescribe medication dictated by your servant if for no other reason that I don't know what to prescribe. Now that I have examined you I can tell you your prolonged periods of mild fever are caused by the chronic inflammation of the tonsils. If I had listened to you I would have been influenced by the authority of the private doctors and would have treated you for heart inflammation. That's what you came to see me about the first time you were here. Also I find your behaviour inconsiderate. You are not so ill to justify asking for a doctor's visit, and send your servant for a prescription. Even today you were able to go out for an X ray, yet unable to come and see me at the surgery. I wonder if you would ask your private doctor to come and visit you at home? You keep asking for visits because they cost you nothing."

While I was talking the patient tried several times to interrupt me. When I finished, she asked: "So you think there's nothing wrong with my heart? Dr N. told me I suffer from inflammation of the heart."

I was stunned. For half an hour I've been trying to examine her, explain what was wrong, and this was the result. I spoke again, this time in a raised voice.

"There is nothing wrong with your heart. I have examined you six times. Also I have X ray images to prove it. I am unable to comment on the ludicrous opinions of others. I have explained what is wrong with you. You should see a laryngologist. Unless there are any changes in your condition please do not ask me to visit you again. Since you can manage to go out on other business you can easily make the effort to come see me."

The lady was not perturbed by my words.

"I am incapable of spite," she said. "I am too well bred to offend anyone."

I had no strength left to reply. I shook this charming lady's hand and ran and ran, because I was afraid that if we continued this "interesting" conversation it would go on to this day with the obvious result of leaving neither of us satisfied.

Profession – actress

While working for the Warsaw Social Insurance it is difficult not to come across this kind of profession. When a patient comes to see me heavily made-up and hands me a brown-coloured membership card marked "professional" signed by owners of various night clubs that change every month, I know when I ask 'what is your profession' the inevitable answer would be 'actress'. Those actresses or nightclub dancers were not in the first flush of youth, usually around thirty, rarely twenty-eight. I seldom saw anyone younger.

One day, while examining a patient, I did not check her membership card beforehand. I saw a huge scar on her chest, the result of the removal of several ribs. I was greatly surprised when she told me she was a dancer. I just could not understand how she could work in cabarets

94

with such a deformed chest. In one place there were three ribs missing and a very deep scar.

"Oh, I have costumes that cover it up completely," she said. "It doesn't show at all."

"But how can you carry on in this type of work in your fragile state? The lung adhesions must be painful as you breathe."

"Actually it's one of the easiest jobs I can manage," she said.

Evidently this kind of work is not hard since I was called to see a sixteen year old child, also a cabaret dancer. I say 'child' because as it turned out she was younger than sixteen, very thin, not fully developed, suffering from acute appendicitis. She wasn't bad looking, but heavy make-up and brightly coloured nails betrayed her profession. Her condition was serious. I referred her straight away as a surgical emergency.

I looked around her room. The door opened directly on the staircase, in place of honour stood piles of empty chocolate boxes. Was this 'child' rewarded with chocolates? In spite of her serious condition I was tempted to contact Social Services. As though in answer to my thoughts there appeared a policeman in uniform and told me he had telephoned the emergency services as I had requested and was taking his sister to the hospital this very minute.

On her return from the hospital the girl asked for a visit from me. The scar after the operation was fairly big, but more importantly I diagnosed a malfunction of the heart. That was two years ago. What happened to this cabaret dancer I don't know.

It just so happened that all the cabaret dancers who came to see me had surgical problems of one kind or another. One of the "actresses" had the following accident:

She was returning home on the night of the New Year's Eve when she was hit by a taxi crossing the road. An ambulance took her home and the next day she called me.

She lived in two rooms on the fifth floor. (Oh, those fifth floors in blocks without a lift!). She shared them with her mother who said she was a doctor's widow. In the rooms hung with little lace curtains, were stacks of cushions, piles of embroidery, lots of rubbish and flowers. To write a prescription I had to clear the bedside table of three framed photographs, a vase made of shells and a box of chocolates, of course. Hovering over me was an elderly man who said he was the patient's uncle. One of the framed photographs showed my patient in a dancing pose, completely naked. It was pointed to me by this uncle to admire how beautifully his niece can dance.

"And what will become of her now?" he asked anxiously.

I tried to cheer him up.

"I am just about to write a prescription. She has a badly weakened heart muscle which might have been caused by the shock of the accident," then I had a brainwave and asked her a question. "Maybe you had too much to drink that night?"

She shrugged. It confirmed my suspicion she must have been drunk on leaving the bar where she 'danced', and fell under the taxi.

"Never mind how it happened," I said. "I suspect when the taxi hit you with the bumper and knocked you down, it not only weakened your heart muscle, but may have caused a crack in the hip bone. I am contacting a surgeon who will come and examine you."

The surgeon sent her for an X ray. In order to do that the Social Insurance had to carry her down five floors and then bring her up those five floors again. As it happened, she did have a cracked hip bone. The surgeon visited her several times, while I had to treat her heart problem. She was able to get up after two months.

I would have forgotten about the incident, but for the frequent telephone calls from the Social Insurance offices asking to send in her health records. She was suing the owner of the taxi claiming damages and needed proof. But what a lot of bad luck there is in this world! A machine cuts off a workman's hand, a dancer breaks her leg.

*

"What sort of dubious people come here?" asked a patient indignantly, the wife of a treasury office clerk. "I've been waiting for half an hour for my turn when this woman comes, not wearing a hat, no stockings (it was summer), and asks me if she could go in first, skipping the queue. My husband's coming home in two hours' time expecting his dinner; I still have to go to the pharmacy. I refused. She got angry, sat on the arm of the sofa, pretending to read a paper, and started to cough in my direction. Spat all over me. What sort of behaviour is that, I say to her.

You are sitting on the arm of the sofa, you are breaking the furniture. She just turned away and continued to cough."

"What unfriendly people come here!" exclaimed the 'cabaret dancer' when her turn came to see me. Ah, so this was the Miss Z. my previous patient was talking about. Miss Z. continued:

"I dance in the cinema in Wola (district of Warsaw). We start at eight pm. I asked this cow to let me go first as I'm late. She not only refused but lectured me on how to behave."

It was a good thing the two ladies did not come to blows. I would have had to take on the role of a judge and who knows, I might have been hurt in the process.

The Ministry of Foreign Affairs

'This is the Ministry of Foreign Affairs," a voice on the telephone informed me. In that moment my spirit soared with joy. At last I will be granted a passport to enable me to travel abroad. I so wanted to visit Germany. I calmed down a moment later.

"Who am I speaking to?"

"I am your patient from Orłowska Street. You have been treating me for an inflammation of the stomach."

My vision of foreign travel disappeared in a mist.

"How can I help you?" I asked politely.

There followed a detailed explanation. The wife of this clerk in the Ministry went to visit her aunt in the country. Her husband is alone at home, ill and doesn't know what to do, he has diarrhoea, high temperature and nausea.

"I'll go and see him in a couple of hours."

The patient had a slightly raised temperature, but complained about everything. The worst thing was he had to sit an exam in five days' time in order to be eligible for a prestigious posting to one of the offices abroad. Maybe Paris. He badly wanted to be posted abroad, but the very thought of an exam put him in a state of panic. He asked me to write him a letter to excuse him from taking the exam given the poor state of his health.

"But the Social Insurance does not issue such notes. And, at any rate, I don't know how you will feel in five days' time. Right now you are not seriously ill. Here is a prescription for your diarrhoea."

The next day he asked for a visit – on the sixth floor. Luckily this was the only block of flats in my district with a lift. He told me there was no improvement. He was suffering from a state of acute anxiety, palpitations, diarrhoea. I gave in and wrote a note on my private letter headed paper that the patient is sick and will probably not be able to sit the exam in three days' time. I also advised him to send a telegraph to his wife.

Two months later I met him on a street with his wife and daughter. He came up to me and thanked me warmly for the sick note.

"I must admit I did not use it, because three days later I did go and sat the exam. Having that note in my pocket stating I was sick made me relaxed, I felt if I didn't know something I could always show it to my examiners to show that I was sick and not because I was ill prepared. I passed and have been offered a place abroad in France. Unfortunately not in Paris – but still."

Saying goodbye I reflected how we, the Social Insurance doctors, have to cope with situations on such a wide scale, ranging from cabaret dancers in night clubs and ending with urbane clerks from the Ministry of Foreign Affairs with academic qualifications.

Confidence Gained

I always emphasise the difference between the Social Insurance patients from the provinces with those in Warsaw. In Warsaw every so-called "better-off" person does not consider a doctor like me seriously. He goes to a private doctor, or says he does. How good that sounds! How many times I heard from a patient who has just come in to my consulting room 'I used to see Dr.A. privately, you've probably heard of him'. On the contrary, I have not, I have not been in Warsaw for many years. How and where was I supposed to meet my colleagues, particularly the 'private' ones?

A patient would then look askance at me. He is asking me for the medication prescribed by Dr. A. If the medicine contains ingredients made in this country and if I agree, I will then transfer the prescription onto the Social Insurance form. I know from experience the patient will come to see me again sooner or later and continue to complain, something he has no courage to do when being seen by private doctors.

It gets worse when a patient brings a prescription from a private doctor not accepted by the Social Insurance. Then follow numerous appeals to the Chief Medical Officer, and the unending complaints "What am I paying all this money for?" Any assurances that the medication we prescribe is the same, the only difference is that it must be manufactured in this country, leaves a patient dissatisfied. He must have exactly the same medicine. This atmosphere of dissatisfaction I try to quash with great difficulty every day.

But there are patients I remember with pleasure who, even though they could afford to pay high fees for private treatment, do not mention it when they come to see me, and are happy when they have recovered thanks to the Social Insurance prescriptions.

A wife of a director of one of the Warsaw factories fell seriously ill with a heart complaint. There was not a prominent specialist left in Warsaw her husband had failed to take her to. I've no idea how the couple ended up in my consulting room. On that day there were a particularly large number of people waiting to be seen. It often happens there might be fifteen patients coming all at the same time and still more joining them, at other times they "drip in" one every ten minutes. Then it is straightforward to see patients in order, but otherwise it is very difficult to sort it out. When I try to move the extra patients to the next day there is such a disturbance and fuss it is better to deal with them even perfunctorily on the day and move them to the following one for proper examination.

On seeing the director and his wife in the waiting room I explained it would be better if they could come the next day at an appointed time. I would then have more time to listen and examine, and it would be easier for me too, because how can I concentrate when another loud disturbance or quarrel might erupt in the waiting room about whose turn is next, or about re-prescribing private prescriptions, or about membership cards, or whatever.

The greatest disagreements between patient and doctor had to do with administrative concerns, such as a patient losing his membership card, or had lost his right to various treatments because he failed to tell the doctor he had been unemployed for three weeks, and other similar ones. All those problems would erupt in loud confrontations in the doctor's consulting room.

The sick lady agreed and came the next day. I prescribed calming drops for her heart. She came back three days later. From what she told me it seemed that everything had been tried. She changed her doctors often and that was probably the reason of her steadily worsening condition. I told her honestly what I thought: I explained that even the most highly respected doctor cannot prescribe the right medication the first time and not be given the opportunity to follow the patient up. I found out she could not tolerate medicines containing the lily of the valley. The lily of the valley is a well known treatment for the heart.

I examined her carefully, sent her for an X ray, even sent her to a consultant specialist asking for confirmation of my diagnosis. She put up with all of this without complaint even though I knew she was kept waiting in my waiting room. She was given forty injections of iodine and a combination of strengthening and calming medication for the heart. The treatment was successful.

When a year later she caught a cold she asked for a visit. I was away at the time and my locum did not want to prescribe the medication I had prescribed for her.

As the result the lady went back to one of her private doctors. She told me later he could not get over the fact how much her health had improved. A year ago her state of health was serious, now she was only suffering from a cold, asking for the medicine I had prescribed at the time. It was an ordinary creosote syrup approved by the Social Insurance which my replacement colleague would not prescribe, so she asked the private doctor for it. And here is the crux of the matter. She was prescribed a Famel syrup because the private doctor could not prescribe a Social Insurance syrup. The patient complained.

"There was not much I could do, I had to drink it," she said. "There was nothing else. But it's not a patch on the one you prescribed, just a few spoonfuls and the cough was gone."

For an experienced Social Insurance doctor to make a diagnosis is easy thanks to access to laboratories, X rays and medication, because

100

the Social Insurance Formulary contains all the elements which one can mix in a number of different ways. The most difficult part is to gain a patient's trust, and for that one should fight with all possible means.

A grateful old lady

There was not a day in February, March and April of 1936 when I did not have to climb three flights of stairs to visit an old lady suffering from bronchial pneumonia and pyelonephritis. She was seventy-six. I was interested in her case and determined to keep her alive. Twice a day a hospital nurse would come to give her injections and flush her bladder. I had also asked for the assistance of a urologist who visited her several times. Her pneumonia returned three times. At long last, around Easter time, her health began to improve. I can't remember how many urine analyses were carried out by the Social Insurance, but the latest one showed improvement, and the bronchial pneumonia had already gone.

The old lady was an intelligent woman, always with a book in her hand. Her son was a metal worker in the state factory making aeroplanes. Her daughter-in-law was a good home maker and took good care of her mother-in-law. With the coming of Easter she baked a lot of cakes and prepared a variety of meats.

When I saw those Easter preparations I thought – all we need now for the old lady to eat too much ham or go to church and the three months of treatment will go down the drain. I warned them as emphatically as I could. They did listen, the old lady ate little, and nothing from the festive table. After Easter she came to see me asking to sign a piece of paper.

"What is this?"

"This is a note to St. Teresa of the Roses to thank her for my miraculous cure, but the priest doesn't want to publish it in the "Knights of the Virgin" (a religious monthly publication) without a doctor's certificate showing what illness I was suffering from. Nobody believes that one could possibly recover from both pneumonia and kidney failure at my age. When people read about my recovery they will pray to St. Teresa of the Roses even more."

I did write the certificate. But the old lady ignores me when we pass on the street. I saw her yesterday.

*

The situation of old people forced to depend for the remainder of their lives on their children (or son-in-law) who don't love them is very hard indeed. I looked after such people, prolonging their lives with a pinch of digitalis, a few injections or camphor, only to send them back to their wretched existence. In a one-room household they would share it with their children or grandchildren, or sleep in the kitchen. I have heard many complaints and grudges from both sides.

"So what did we take her in for?" asked one daughter-in-law of a sick old woman I came to visit, lying in bed near the kitchen, when I said she was too weak to work and needed to rest. "We thought rather than pay a servant we'd take in family, give her food and lodging. Now we are out of pocket."

The old lady despaired: "They expect me to cook their meals, go to the market, do the shopping. I've no strength left. What will happen to me? That digitalis did me a lot of good."

These old people I cared for, having already called the priest to administer the Last Rites then recovered when they drank several bottles of medicines. Their return to health was not always a source of joy for the family.

In one case a urologist admitted a patient to the hospital because she was incontinent as a result of inflammation. She was continually leaking urine and the smell around her was truly awful. After three months, the period when the right to medical care expired, she was sent home. Her daughter-in-law arrived, almost accusing me.

"What are we to do now with the old trout? The Social Insurance doesn't want to keep her in the hospital, once she gets home she'd be pissing all over again."

I decided to ask her back: "And what will happen if you find yourself in a similar situation in thirty years time? What will your children do for you?"

The woman left indignant. "I came for advice, not a lecture on morals."

I remember another old man, age about seventy. His wife, an office cleaner, twenty-five years younger than him, was the wage earner. She had a completely different attitude towards her husband old enough to be her father. He had been suffering from emphysema. I was only called in later once he qualified for care as before that he, as a family member, was not covered by the Insurance in the prescribed period. The cleaner asked for visits frequently because her husband was suffering from weakened cardiac muscle. He recovered with the help of various injections administered by the hospital nurses. I met them both then. She was smartly dressed, looking around forty although she must have been older, he a bent old man. They came to thank me personally for the care and medication. They both looked happy. It was obvious his recovery was not a tragedy for the family as it was in the cases which I had described.

I remember also an old lady who would continually ask questions. She had a lump on her bladder and was seeing a specialist. She was financially supported by her son who looked after her well. Her questions hid boasting.

"My son has bought me half a kilo of bananas. Do you think they are good for me?"

"He made me a semolina pudding. Will it be all right to eat it?"

"My son has just bought a fish, ever so fresh, just for me. Will it upset my digestion?"

She told me the doctors in the outpatients department where she went for her treatment were not polite because they would not answer her questions and told her to go and see her GP.

Oh, all right, I went along with it, she was pleasant enough. Let her consult three times just to ask if the fresh salad her son bought was good for her digestion. I tried to cope with her garrulousness with equanimity.

On the whole the old people were satisfied with the Social Insurance, otherwise what would happen to them? Their children had no means to support them for long, and could not afford the modern, up-to-date treatments.

Once I was called to see an old woman privately. Her daughter told me straightaway that she only called me so that at the end of my visit I would be able to fill in the death certificate. I examined an eighty-two year old semi-conscious woman, administered an injection for the heart and prescribed some medication. The *"loving"* daughter came to ask me for the death certificate only eleven days later. In the course of conversation she admitted the old woman had recovered consciousness and asked for a visit from me, but they could not afford another bottle of medicine or another private consultation. They had no Social Insurance cover.

I also came across a case of an old woman, wife of a labourer, who had a cyst on her ovaries for twenty years. Her husband absolutely forbade her to have an operation. In the sixty-fifth year of her life the cyst began to swell caused by a fluid collecting inside it. There was no question of an operation on account of her age, and also, because this married couple would not change their views on *"cutting"* and hospitals, insisting on staying at home. She lived on the fifth floor in a block of flats opposite mine.

The gynaecologist said there was nothing more he could do. It was likely the swelling cyst would *"choke"* her. I asked my surgeon colleague to drain it through the stomach lining. The neighbour then told me the doctor drained about half-a bucket of fluid out of her.

When the fluid collected again he repeated it about six more times. All this lasted around seven months. Once drained the sick woman was even able to get up. This present of seven months of life was given to her thanks to a doctor's skill. But could her husband, a labourer after thirty years of working life, be able to afford that kind of treatment if he did not belong to the Social Insurance?

Marital Confidences

A doctor is expected to listen to his patients' marital problems. It seems to me that the unpopularity of a Social Insurance doctor stems from the limited time he/she can devote to listen to the various conflicts between wife and husband. I am only able to touch on them when a patient suffers from vague ailments. With the intelligentsia I have always managed to come to some understanding, helped by resorting to psychotherapy. With the simple women suffering from sexual neurasthenia it was more difficult. One of those patients clearly stated:

104

"I am sure I'll recover more quickly if I was examined by a "man"".

"That sort of complaint is not covered by the Social Insurance," was my curt response.

It was a different story with the intelligentsia. Once a lady came to see me. She had been married for a year. This was the beginning of summer, there were not many patients in my waiting room and I was able to devote more time to her. While I was examining her, having found nothing apart from fatigue and exhaustion, she began to cry:

"What is the matter?" I asked, feeling sorry for her.

"It's my husband, he is so unkind," she began, tears dripping on her hands holding a handkerchief already wet. She began to tell me her story.

She married a widower with three grown-up children ages ranging from eighteen to twenty-two. Three months ago she gave birth to a baby boy whom she adored. She did everything for him herself, would not allow anyone else touch him. Her husband, on the other hand, showed her no interest at all. He wanted to go on holiday on his own. Before her marriage she was an agricultural instructress and had earned good salary . She'd have loved to start to work again, but had no one to leave the baby with.

"And your husband – did he think you too should go on holiday with the baby?"

"Oh yes, he did. He even told me to go and stay with my relatives in the country, but he won't let me go back to work."

I thought about this for a while and began to explain as gently as I could: "I must admit I think your husband is right. I hope you won't think I am giving you a bad advice, but I think your situation at home is like this. Your husband has a responsible position at work which is tiring and stressful. You and the baby need rest, but so does your husband. Probably your husband has liver problems."

The woman nodded. (Where did I learn the art of clairvoyance?)

"There you are then," I continued. "Your husband is probably going for treatment. Please stop crying, it's so bad for complexion. Do go to your relatives in the country to rest and build up your strength. On your return when you and the baby feel well, you could start looking for a job and find a nanny for the baby. You will look refreshed and well and I am sure your husband's attitude will change. Men don't like a quiet, hopeless, resigned look. Be more lively. If you want my advice I suggest you should try showing your husband a happy, smiling face."

The lady looked surprised and slightly offended.

"Am I supposed to go out of my way to please him?"

"But then why should he go out of his way to please you? If you demand something from somebody you need to give something in return. A husband should feel happy in your company. Do think about that. I must stress, my remarks are well intended, prompted by great feelings of sympathy towards you. I hope I have not upset you."

We parted amicably. I know she did go with the baby for a holiday. What happened to her later, I could not find out because she registered with another GP when I was allotted to a different catchment area.

*

On the way home, around 10 o'clock I saw a crowd of people in front of the gate of the block of flats next to mine. Outside was an ambulance, the crowd was cursing and shouting.

"You bastard! It's your mistress!"

The next day I was called to the block where the crowd had gathered the previous day. I found a woman in bed, pretty and polite. She had an attack of gall stones. Yesterday she called for an ambulance. They gave her an injection, now she asked for a visit from a GP because she wanted to continue with the treatment.

She was Russian, five years older than her husband who was habitually unfaithful to her. The previous evening on her return home she found him with a woman again. She threw the girl out, but after the row felt ill. Indeed, I found an enlarged liver. I advised rest and prescribed a medication.

"Please doctor, will you tell my husband his behaviour is killing me?" she begged.

"Of course I will. Ask him to come and see me."

To my surprise an exceptionally handsome young man did come. Dark hair, big, blue eyes, neatly clipped moustache. I could just imagine what devastation this Don Juan, brimming with energy, brought to the hearts of ladies in Powiśle.[15]

Note 15: District of Warsaw

106

I felt sorry for his Russian wife. What was I supposed to say to this licentious man? I said something to the effect that his wife loved him, that his behaviour is affecting her health. I was looking straight into the eyes of this Adonis, not believing for a moment that my arguments carried any conviction. But, wonder of wonders, rows in that apartment stopped. The Russian lady came to thank me for talking to her husband.

"I work all day in school serving meals to poor children. I am also fostering a girl. My husband has settled down. But I am very depressed. I don't think my liver will ever get better. Ten days ago the Bolsheviks shot my brother. I received a letter from my sister-in-law, posted from B.(a town in Poland). Who sent it from B. I don't know. My uncle was shot in Siberia six months ago – I only read about it in the papers."

"I thought only prominent citizens were shot in Russia,' I said. 'What did your brother and your uncle do?"

"Nothing. They had a farm and lived off that. Five years ago they were moved to Siberia. Ten days ago my brother was shot. My sister-in-law is left without any means of support. She has four children. So I think maybe it's better to have a husband like mine, who is more like a friend doing …well you know what he does, than to live in Russia."

"Yes, you are right," I sighed and reflected – is there any occurrence on this earth in which a Warsaw GP will not be involved?

Now I am living in expectations of listening to my patients' stories from the Japanese-Chinese and Spanish wars.

It's not a bed of roses

That day my heart hurt badly. It was an effort to visit six patients in town. "Careful now," I said to myself. "Your heart is an unreliable tool." I was counting the hours to the end of the working day. It was an effort to bend over a patient or to stretch to take down their records. At last it was 6 o'clock, the end of surgery when I could rest. I told the servant this is the end for today, don't let anyone in. I went to lie down. I was about to fall asleep when the door bell started to ring.

"A gentleman," said the servant, reporting that he didn't look sick. "He just wants to see you, needs some information."

The servant told him he could only see the doctor during consulting

107

hours and right now the doctor was not at home. In response the man continued to ring the bell. My heart was getting worse, I was afraid it might be an onset of a heart attack. The servant disconnected the bell to stop it from ringing. The man began to kick the door and only stopped when told she had phoned for the police.

He arrived the next day three minutes before 6 o'clock. There were still five patients in the waiting room. The servant didn't want to let him in, but as he only needed information and no treatment she relented. His turn came at 6.45 when I finished seeing those five patients. He said he was a lawyer, unemployed, working for some philanthropic organisation. He had no membership card only a certificate. He had suffered from some venereal complaint contracted in the past and asked for a form to see a specialist.

"But you could have gone to the specialist directly. Patients suffering from venereal diseases do not require a form from the GP. There was no need to make a scene and create that hellish commotion."

I mention my heart attack, my restless night, and many more nights when I could not sleep worrying about various problems in connection with my profession. A Social Insurance doctor's life is no bed of roses.

About cobblers, print-setters and TB in Warsaw

In the district covered by my practice live people employed in various first-rate Warsaw enterprises – hospitality, merchant, tailoring, cobblers and print-setters. As their doctor I was able to be acquainted with the lives of those qualified Polish workers. Oh, how poor, how badly organised their lives were! On the whole they earned good wages. On their medical cards I even saw a figure of 150 zl. a week.[16] It would seem they had enough money to live on, comparable with the salaries of professionals. And yet cobblers lived frequently in one-room lodgings in basements or in garrets in old, dilapidated wooden houses. But their wives – ah, those cobblers' wives! One might be sitting in my consulting room, waiting her turn, talking non-stop, of course.

Note 16: Value in today's terms – 2,550zl = £510

"I am not just anybody, you know," she'd be saying. "I come from a better class of people. I am here because my husband's been paying those subscriptions. And what do I get for them, I ask you. I suffer from asthma. I was in hospital, they put it right, I get home and it's back again. Why can they cure it privately and the Social Insurance can't, that's what I want to know."

The print-setters were different. They lived in decent housing, sent their children to high school. Unfortunately that's where TB was prevalent. Not long ago I went to see a patient with 'flu. Three days later he spat out blood. I sent the sputum for analysis. Back came the result showing bacilli – 3-4 in the field of vision, active TB. The man was supporting his 15-year old daughter, wife and mother.

"You must go away to the sanatorium. Social Insurance will pay the cost," I told him. "Your family will have to tighten their belts for the next two months, but you mustn't worry, they won't starve. By that time you will be cured and not infect anybody, particularly your 15-year old daughter. I know you will understand that's what you need to do, not like the cobbler earning the same money as you who came to see me today. His wife has been infected for the last six years, he's been spitting blood, but still has not moved out of his damp basement, even though he's been coughing for the last six months and only came to see me now."

Anyone looking into the interiors of those lodgings, particularly the basements in the district of Powiśle, will see the reason for the widespread incidents of TB. When will we reach the stage when all those houses will be pulled down and replaced by new, clean and bright ones, with no damp basements?!

Comments

There is no end of stories of diseases, of doctors' successes and disappointments, life just goes on regardless. Every moment a new human being comes into the world and almost every instant another dies. Both require doctors' intervention. It is only worthwhile to write about them if one can draw some conclusions.

Through my work for the Social Insurance I intervene in human life. Thanks to it I need not involve myself in the highly disagreeable ceremony of asking for payment after I have examined a patient. This unpleasantness needs to be carried out by private doctors who, after all, need to earn their living. I am not limited by a patient's financial means when it comes to recommending investigations, medication or X rays. When in doubt I can always call on a specialist. In urgent cases I have the hospital at my disposal. All this makes it much easier to make a diagnosis, prescribe medical treatment and obtain favourable results.

However, it is rare indeed for a patient to be satisfied and not complain about the Social Insurance. I have observed thousands of cases and can unequivocally state they have no reason for complaint. Particularly in the capital there is a prevailing atmosphere of discontent. The inhabitants of Warsaw suffer from a snobbery complex at its very worst. Apparently it is 'the done thing' to be seen by Dr 'Achtenovski' [17] – I give that name to the type of doctor who, contrary to medical ethics, helps patients to complain about the Social Insurance, in order to put them on his private list.

I will not forget one curious incident involving a certain elderly gentleman who felt he belonged to the top echelons of society. Both his two sons and his daughter-in-law were doctors. When his wife fell sick he called in a renowned "herbalist" to see her. This "excellent" herbalist took 100 zloty for consultation.[18] In vain did the gentleman argue that it's not done to charge a doctors' family for medical treatment. "His excellency" replied he cannot do otherwise and indeed has done him a favour by charging him only 100 zloty. Having taken the money he diagnosed gastroenteritis. After the patient did not improve, a referral to a surgeon resulted in the diagnosis of a benevolent rectal tumour. The patient recovered after an operation.

The husband was a frequent consulter of mine and told me this story. Based on this, and similar stories, I formed an opinion not only about the Achtenovski doctors, but also about the paying patients who crowd into their waiting rooms and see none of the bluff, nor the playing on their snobbery. Those doctors play up to their paying patients, but there is no reason for them to act all superior to us, the Social Insurance doctors.

Note 17: 'Achtenovski' is a made-up name
Note 18: Present day value 1,700zl=£340

110

I'm somehow not impressed by these Dr Achtenovski types. I can understand if a person is minded to pay 100zl. or even more for a consultation, but there is no reason to look down on those who pay their subscription to the Social Insurance. No monthly subscription comes to 100 zl. Payment of subscriptions entitles a patient not only to GP consultations, but also to various treatments, injections, X rays, radio- and other therapy, the hospital in cases of surgical operations, as well as unemployment and sickness benefits, and an old age pension.

Is the reason for complaints based on the fact that unlike the Achtenovski doctor, a Social Insurance doctor might not instantly pamper a patient? And if the treatment from a Social Insurance doctor does not result immediately in the desired effect, would Dr Achtenovski be able to perform miracles? The issue comes down to respect in a doctor's abilities. If a patient comes already convinced that a Social Insurance doctor is useless, how can that doctor build confidence, especially in cases when patients reject the prescribed medication because they can afford the privately prescribed ones. Is the Social Insurance doctor supposed to apologise to them that he is not the one whom they can trust? Frankly, who do those "estimable" people respect? I wonder.

In Poznań patients could freely choose their GP - a system that existed for ten years. As the result a patient had "confidence" in all doctors by changing their GP at least once a month curious to find out how one doctor's treatment differs from another's.

One should approach a doctor amicably and respectfully, and he will be amply repaid.

There is one other thing which destroys the doctor/patient relationship and that is the bureaucracy doctors have to manage. I had a case where a patient did not have treatment because he had an out of date membership card of the old type, while the Social Insurance insisted on a new one. He got very upset and had private treatment for the next two years. Only when he died his wife regretfully admitted his death was caused by that membership card, because he was determined not to renew it, and I could not treat him on the old one. I was of the opinion her husband would have died anyway because he suffered from infarct of the heart but, who knows, he might not have been so embittered in his last days by having to pay for a costly private treatment.

The patients' ignorance of the regulations is no cause for joy to the Social Insurance either. A patient doesn't know who his GP is because he can't be bothered to look at the notice board hanging by the gate of his block. Instead he runs from one GP to another complaining about the Social Insurance. Also, it does not occur to him a doctor is a human being who works during the day and sleeps at night. He will often call a doctor during the night or in the evening because it is easier and, after all, more simple, to call a GP than the emergency services. Often he forgets to sign the membership card or fails to register the change of address even though asked to do so by the GP who will see him just this once without it. When he finds himself in a waiting room he thinks he is the only one pressed for time and all the others can wait an extra half hour so that he can be admitted first.

Those are the most frequent causes of disturbances in a doctor's consulting room and grumbles about the Social Insurance. Are they serious? Certainly not. All could be easily dealt with a modicum of goodwill, familiarity with the regulations, and just a tiny dose of respect for the GP and the institution which employs them, the Social Insurance.

Warsaw 30 March 1938

Warsaw before the Second World War

Warsaw – Łazienki Park: Where the lady suffering from cancer so wanted to go with Dr Sabina in a horse-drawn cab

S ⚔ P
DR MED.
SABINY RÓŻYCKIEJ
zе SKOPIŃSKICH ps. „SABINA"
ŻŁNIERZA IV REJONU AK W-WA ŚRÓDM. ODPRAWIONE ZOS-
WIE Dn. 14. XI godz 10°° NABOŻEŃSTWO ZAŁOBNE w KOSCIELE
U. TERESY przy UL. TAMKA 4 A
A KTÓRE ZAPRASZAJĄ WSZYSTKICH ZYCZLIWYCH PAMIĘCI
)LEGŁEJ ZA OJCZYZNĘ

NIEOBECNY SYN, RODZINA : TOWARZYSZE BRONI

OŻENIE WIEŃCA NA GROBIE dn. 14 godz. 14 CMENTARZ
WĄZKOWSKI – ZBIÓRKA przy IV BRAMIE

On the 25th anniversary of the death of Dr.Med. Sabina Różycka nee Skopińska, pseudonym "Sabina", martyred by the Gestapo, combatant of the IV District A.K. (Home Army) Warsaw Central
A funeral service will be held on 14th November at 10 am in the Church of St.Teresa, 4A Tamka (Street) to which all who cherish the memory of those who died for their country are invited by her son from overseas, family and com-rades-in-arms.
A wreath will be laid on her grave on the 14th at 1400 hours. Meet at Powązki cemetery, Gate IV

113

Dr. Monika Blackwell

A second Doctor's Diary

I first read my Grandmother's book aged about twelve and I particularly remember reading her opening sentence about having conducted about 100,000 consultations. I have no idea how many I've done, but I've been working now as a GP for twenty three years, having qualified as a doctor twenty-nine years ago, so I suspect I'm not far off that myself.

Dr. Monika Blackwell
Graduation photograph

I started my medical studies at Charing Cross and Westminster Medical School in October 1985.

I used to joke that I was there because that's where I was born (my mother gave birth to me within sound of Big Ben at Westminster Hospital eighteen years previously). On my first day we all crowded into a large lecture theatre where the Dean berated us for looking like football hooligans. He then suggested that we each looked to our left, then to our right and remembered who was there because by the end of the year, one of those people would not be here anymore. I think about a quarter of my intake did not pass the course in the end. Given the sacrifices I had already made to get there, I was determined not to be one of them. Within the first week we had our first dissection class. The huge room was on the top floor of the medical school, somewhat inappropriately overlooking Fulham cemetery. Rows upon rows of trolleys with shrouded bodies were lined up. We were divided into groups of six to a body and learnt anatomy through dissection of it. I recognise now that it is a well known tactic to teach dissociation, but at the time I think there was a realisation that this was it, and that dealing with disease and dying was what made us different from other people.

Pre-clinical studies were, as they were for my grandmother, all about lectures and theory. They lasted for two years and followed a standard academic year of three terms or semesters. We had frequent assignments and exams every term as we grappled with anatomy, physiology, biochemistry and pharmacology in the main (we also did some psychology and sociology: I don't recall that we did much ethics, let alone the structure of the NHS). We didn't see any patients and were envious of the older medical students in their short white coats indicating that they were studying on the wards. On the wards were teams of doctors known as Firms. They were headed by a Consultant specialist, then there was a Registrar and possibly a Senior Registrar, plus a couple or maybe more, of Senior House Officers, and finally the House Officer who had just passed his or her medical school final exams but was not yet fully registered as a doctor. House Officers generally looked the most exhausted and usually had the greatest number of bleeps clipped to their pockets. Bleeps were a way of calling you to the phone – it would ring, and a tiny screen would tell you the number of the person who was trying to get hold of you. The 'Crash Bleep' was for cases of cardiac arrest- it sounded an alarm whereby a robotic voice instructed the hapless holder to run to Ward 6 or wherever.

Clinical studies lasted for three years and were made up of sections of about eight weeks running into each other consecutively. If you wanted to have a break for a week it was at the expense of missing one of, say, a psychiatry attachment. As medical students, we would try to find interesting patients to talk to and practice taking a history, performing an examination then presenting the patient at ward rounds. We'd also sit in clinics or at the edges of operating theatres, and try to pick up some practical skills. I think I helped deliver about twenty babies during my time as a medical student.

While I was still at school, my father showed me an advert in the paper which asked the question – *'What can the Army offer a medical student apart from £6,000 per year?'* I answered that advert, and was successful in my application. It meant that I was commissioned in 1987 as a 2nd Lieutenant and received a small bursary for the last three years of medical school. After I was fully qualified, I served a six year Short Service Commission with the Royal Army Medical Corps (RAMC), leaving in 1998.

I worked hard in medical school but wasn't particularly enamoured of any specialty that we trained in, and was even more put off by some of the doctors I came across. I think I knew what I didn't want to do as a doctor much more than I knew what I did want to do. I did enjoy psychiatry, but decided against it when one consultant declared that the only reason soldiers ever went over the top in the trenches during the First World War was because they'd been given hallucinogenic drugs. My friend and I (both RAMC cadets) thought it was incredible that patriotism never seemed to have crossed his mind.

In my fourth year of medical school I spent a few weeks on an attachment in Washington, USA and saw trauma surgery in a hospital that had Capitol Hill in its catchment area (at the time it had one of the highest numbers of gunshot injuries in the States). The first time I saw an x ray with a bullet on it sticks in my mind. The bullet is so white (radio-opaque) even compared to bone and you could see the track from fragments of metal and fabric. The experience was such that I thought I wanted to specialise in trauma surgery after that. After my final exams, I took six months off and went to learn some more by volunteering at Baragwaneth Hospital, Soweto, South Africa, where I met some inspiring surgeons doing incredible work under the most trying circumstances. I came down to earth with a bump on my return to the UK when my bosses during my surgical house job were not particularly interested in teaching or mentoring. One of my favourite sayings is from Hippocrates – *"Life is short, but the art of healing is long"*. Medicine is fundamentally an apprenticeship where you learn by watching how others do it. It helps enormously if you have teachers who are prepared to take you under their wing. This is particularly true of the practical specialties such as surgery, where the best way to learn is to do it, but it takes time, so anaesthetists and operating theatre managers have to be aware of this and plan it into the schedule. Also it helps if you get a personal recommendation from your consultant as you progress from House Officer to Senior House Officer. Some jobs in hospitals are particularly sought after because they are thought to be good stepping stones up the career ladder. The reverse was also thought to be true, that if you ended up in a district general hospital in the back of beyond, then you wouldn't ever make it to the higher echelons. I think London Medical Schools were particularly prone to be snobby about this.

Somewhere along the line I remember sitting next to my friend who said that she was going to train to be an eye surgeon and I said that General Practice was for me. I think I liked the idea of not having to make my mind up about one particular specialty and that you could treat the whole patient as a person. When it comes to clinicians entrusted with teaching, it's interesting looking back on it how many taught by humiliation rather than by support and encouragement. The most supportive and inspiring teachers I ever met were GPs – and one of them continued to teach me even when I was qualified as a GP. I still remember them to this day.

Overall I felt I was not particularly well prepared for my professional life and only recently actively embraced the joy of a job well done. Interesting isn't it? After all these years I realise I have a good memory for the spoken word which is very useful as patients tell you their stories, and also I have a knack for diagnosis. I think it is a little like solving a puzzle. By listening carefully I add in information from here and there to come to my conclusion. It's usually said that you can make a diagnosis from the patient's history if you listen hard enough, but of course patients don't necessarily know what is important to me, let alone the order in which to say it. I, in turn, have to remember to answer their questions about what worries them. I can be very proud of myself, a little like a magician for arriving at the *"correct answer"*, only for the patient to remain frustrated because their concerns have not been met.

There are about a million consultations per week taking place in a GP setting in the UK. GPs don't make the diagnosis in about a third of them so there are a lot of unhappy patients out there. Add to this, of course, that some things are just unexplained given our current understanding, and one can see why it is a lifelong quest to learn and develop.

I suppose my maxim for my work is to do unto others as I would wish to be done to, and I think this has stood me well. There seems to be much more emphasis when teaching young people these days about emotional intelligence – learning about feelings, motivation, how to deal with setbacks and self-awareness. Well, there wasn't any of that in my day. School was for learning facts and I'm not knocking it. I would have liked to have learnt more about how to think, but here's the thing - learning stuff is a joy that never goes away, and knowing more each year learning about new developments and new ways of doing things is just great.

After I came back from South Africa I did a year of house jobs (this is what the first year of post medical school used to be known as) and was fully registered as a medical practitioner in February 1992. In July 1992, after completing four months of military training I was posted to Osnabruck, Germany, for my first posting and to start my training as a GP. I spent six months in Bosnia as part of the UN mission to protect the delivery of humanitarian aid, as the country formerly known as Yugoslavia violently ripped itself apart, creating the new countries based on ethnicity of Croatia, Bosnia-Herzegovina and Serbia. Postings in the UK followed, during which time I took further exams in General Practice as well as Obstetrics and Gynaecology. I had a couple of lovely postings during this time – my highlight was 15 months as one of the GPs at the Royal Military Academy Sandhurst, looking after cadets, staff and their families. Another was a posting to Bulford in Salisbury Plain when I had the opportunity to join a crew on board a 60 foot sailing boat and sail it down the North Sea.

Medicine for military doctors covers areas not surprisingly unique to the role – design of refugee camps, triage and evacuation of the injured, travel medicine (including tropical medicine), training in extreme environments, and any number of medicals which aim to ensure that military personnel remain physically and mentally able to perform the roles expected of them. It was an introduction to Occupational Health – the area of medicine where work and the impact it can have on health and vice versa come together. This is barely taught in medical school (I am pretty sure I never had any teaching on it). Thousands of studies of the effectiveness of medication or of an intervention such as a particular surgical technique are done around the world every year. The end point of much research is the change in outcomes such range of movement or cholesterol levels or survival in many cases – only in a tiny number do we measure return to former function or to work as the final aim. I have since obtained a further diploma in the subject and combine work as a GP with one day a week of Occupational Health.

My typical day as a Regimental Medical Officer started with two to three hours of *'Sick Parade'*. Military personnel cannot self certify themselves off from their duties, and can only be excused some or all of their duties by a healthcare professional. I had medics to help me – these were soldiers who had received first aid training as well as the management of self limiting illnesses. They were able to assess and treat a number of patients, which meant that between us we could usually deal with thirty to forty soldiers in a couple of hours. I remember during one of my first *'Sick Parades'* being faced with someone with an ingrowing toe nail and having not the first idea how to help him as my medical training to date had concentrated on major illnesses such as heart attacks and asthma. After a while I became much more proficient in managing these, as well acquiring a lifelong love of musculoskeletal problems.

The second part of the morning was usually taken up by a clinic known as *'Families'*. Military personnel could live with their spouses and children in so called *'married quarters'* -a group of houses more commonly referred to as *'The Patch'*. During my time in the Army, living openly as a homosexual was not allowed, nor was it possible to cohabit outside of marriage. I didn't meet many *'Army husbands'* during my time, but I got to know Army married life well, particularly as I too married a fellow officer and followed him from posting to posting for many years.

Family life as an Army wife or child is an unusual one that most civilians have no idea about. A few years ago a well-known singer and conductor called Gareth Malone created the 'Wives Choir' which drew the spotlight to this very different, and at times, difficult life. The rank of a husband determines a large amount of a social life as there is little encouragement for mixing of ranks. Moving on a frequent basis – which can be every nine to twelve months, is hugely disruptive to the making of long term friends for wives or for their ability to work outside the home. Children's education is often interrupted as they can end up moving schools even mid term. *'Continuous Education Allowance'* or boarding school allowance is given if, as a family, you make the decision to send children to boarding school so that they can get a good education and making, and keeping, some regular friends. I have any number of addresses written in pencil in my notebook as Forces friends send yet another *'change of address'* card. We had what I thought at the time were firm friendships, but we have lost touch since. Moving house so often means you have boxes of curtains in your loft in various sizes which you use when you are allocated another quarter. Also you keep all the boxes the TV and the microwave came in, so they don't get damaged in yet another move. As their GP, you hear tales of anxiety and depression frequently, as wives often do not have easy access to their own families who might be able to offer advice and support. The military unit to which their husband is attached has a large support structure headed up by the Families Officer – all sorts of events and amusements are laid on with the aim of helping with social isolation. But there is no getting away with the fact that some Army wives were once professionally qualified women in their own right reduced to depending on their husband for money and status which is quite at odds with the civilian world. Severe long term health issues affecting wives or children could not be managed in a military setting (attendance at specialist outpatients is difficult if you have to travel from abroad for instance) so these families often made the painful decision to live *'Married Unaccompanied'* while the soldier or officer would attempt to commute as much as he can back and forth from the (civilian) family home. Added to this was the challenge of separation during military exercises and deployments which usually lasted around six months. These were the days before mobile phones became ubiquitous, so staying in touch with each other involved the occasional phone call, but more commonly the writing of letters known as 'blueys' (a single sheet of blue paper was folded up into an envelope and sealed). It was not uncommon for military children when drawing pictures of their families did not include their father. Not surprisingly the divorce rate among military families is even higher than it is for civilian families.

We moved house ten times over fifteen years, before we settled down in Bristol. I spent many years working as a locum GP as I couldn't take up a regular post because I didn't know when we would move on again. I really didn't like this – trying to find a practice using a street map, trying to persuade a computer system to do what I wanted to do, and seeing patients for one and only time, not knowing what the outcome was of that consultation.

Computers became increasingly commonplace in GP settings from about the mid 1990s onwards. These revolutionised how we recorded our consultations – there was no more trying to decipher someone else's handwriting (doctors are known for having appalling handwriting), it was much easier to find individual patient records and also to carry out audits and reviews. Medical computing is so sophisticated now that we manage all our appointments on them as well as being able to send texts or carry out online consultations and finding a huge amount of data. A couple of years ago I decided to spend a day with a hospital consultant in his clinic. He then he came to sit in my surgery in turn. I was amazed at how much more primitive hospital medical computing records are compared to ours. I believe that NHS GP records known as 'Lloyd George Envelopes' are no longer being used now that all primary care records are computerised. Being so computer-dependent for our work now means that there is often a third 'person' in the room when you are with a patient. I am aware that many patients say that often doctors don't even look at them but only at the computer screen. We have a different way of working now (of which more later) which means that I have often looked up the information I need before I see a patient face to face, while still aware that I am often looking at a screen as much if not more, than looking at a patient.

I have been at my current practice in Yate, Bristol since 2011, and have been a partner since 2013. My fellow partners and I own the building from which we provide General Practice services. (There is a tendency now to refer to general practice as 'Primary Care' and hospital practice as 'Secondary Care'. These terms are not particularly useful as a lot of people seek help for the first time with a particular problem in the Accident and Emergency Departments of hospitals, while a number of specialist-led services are run from GP practices, which allow use of their rooms for this purpose). We run our practice as a small business, employing over twenty five people and providing care to 11,500 registered patients five days a week. (It's interesting to read my grandmother's description of who her patients were, given that the idea of providing health care to 'insured' people and their families started in Poland in the early 1920s and the NHS on a similar, more nationalised, model in 1948). As a GP Partner I am a so called Independent Contractor – I am contracted to provide General Medical Services to all the patients registered with our practice. We have catchment areas, as Sabina did. We receive a capitation payment which is based on how many patients are registered with us. We are paid slightly different amounts for different populations - the elderly and the very young attract a higher payment than those of working age. In exchange we provide unlimited care to our registered patients which mean there is no limit to the number of times that a patient can request an appointment. Whether they get an appointment is another argument altogether, as the amount we are paid roughly allows for six consultations a year, whereas it is common for the elderly with complex health issues to consult about thirty times a year. We have additional payments made for preventative care (such as childhood vaccinations and cervical smears) as well as for management of long term health issues: for instance, a diabetic patient has to see a nurse to have a review of his medication, a foot check, as well as an eye check, to detect any diabetic damage to qualify for this payment. I am self-employed as Sabina was, and while I have not been bankrupted by tax demands, the rules and regulations around tax for GPs are so complex that accountants have to be specialised in the field, and even the amount of tax I pay twice a year varies widely from year to year.

Managing patient demand is a huge issue both for us, General Practitioners, and for hospitals. Every year it seems there is a 'winter crisis' where there are not enough hospital beds for patients who need one. They end up staying on hospital trolleys for hours on end, before a bed is finally found for them. It's a topic that has been much researched in General Practice. There are those who say that we ration care by making it hard for patients to see us. There are many options for patients to get help. A number of them research their symptoms first on the internet (so called 'Dr Google' which can be helpful, but of course it is an unregulated resource and can just frighten patients unnecessarily). Pharmacists, Minor Injury Units, the telephone based NHS 111 system which uses algorithms to help advise patients - all this is available. We use receptionists to manage our appointments and have trained them to give out results and take requests for repeat prescriptions. We have practice nurses and healthcare assistants for dressings, health checks, monitoring of long term health conditions and blood tests. Even with all of this, a GPs usual working day is eleven to twelve hours long, often involving seeing or speaking to 40-50 patients each day.

Re-reading my grandmother's book all these years later, what strikes me are the similarities in what we do. The differences are striking, of course. It seems as though death has been banished – we don't talk about it very much, laying someone out at home is a thing of the past, and the death of a child is so remarkable and unforgiveable that doctors are publicly denounced or struck off (I'm thinking of Charlie Gard, a child born with a progressive neurological disorder whose parents fought a public battle with the hospital specialists to stop his life support machines being turned off, or Dr Hadiza Bawa-Garda, an experienced paediatrician who was struck off when a child in her care died).

We undergo hours of training to learn how to break bad news to a patient to discuss end of life care with them, because it's such an unnatural thing to do. I don't remember in medical school anyone talking about what happens when someone actually dies. If a death was 'expected', it was dealt with behind closed doors with the help of hospice staff. It's only been in the past year or so that we have been encouraged to talk to patients about 'the ceiling of care' as the general feeling is that we can and must 'do something' at all times. I've lost track of the number of times distraught patients come to the end of chemotherapy treatment and feel that they have been put on the rubbish heap to die. We know that there is a huge disconnect between how effective cancer treatments really are and what patients think they are. Often cancer treatment buys time, but it is rarely curative especially in older patients. What seemingly is often lacking is an honest discussion about how effective and how unpleasant those treatments are, in order for patients to decide if they want to proceed or not.

123

Sabina writes extensively about TB and how it ravaged the lives of young people in particular. TB is so rare now that not only do we have a vaccine effective against it, we no longer need to vaccinate routinely as part of usual childhood vaccination in the UK. We have very effective treatments for it, as well as efficient 'contact tracing' arrangements (which is important as it particularly spreads to close contacts). Two particular patients spring to mind – one was a lady I think in her forties. She had a nasty ulcer that just would not heal and eventually was shown to be caused by TB. Another patient came to see me with a cough which he had had for several weeks – this is usually worrying in itself. Of additional concern was that he was a GP who regularly travelled back to his country of birth, Pakistan, where TB still exists in much higher numbers than here. He was furious when I suggested that he should have a chest X ray to see if he had TB, and accused me of being racist. I just hope that he didn't, especially as he could quite easily have passed it onto his patients.

A big change for me now is the real and unwelcome risk of litigation. I might only spend eight to ten minutes with a patient, and then have to spend another three to four minutes writing up notes. If I don't write extensive notes I could be accused with not having done it, or didn't ask it or I didn't say it. The days of writing 'chest infection, Rx (doctor shorthand for prescription) *Amoxicillin 500mg tds 5/7 (i.e. three times a day for five days)*' are long gone. Instead I usually write about eight to ten lines of notes about how long the symptoms have been there, what my examination findings are (and also what is not present, to show that I have thought of another diagnosis, but have discounted it). In addition I add a line about follow up and what to do if the symptoms get worse.

I have to have insurance in order to practice, and the costs of this until quite recently, were about 10% of my pre-tax income. In fact, there were times when the cost of 'compliance' i.e. insurance, membership of various organisations, attending study days which involved childcare, were so high that it took up almost all of my earned income.

I have to prove, through annual appraisal and fifty hours of 'learning' each year, that I am keeping up to date and indicating on a computerised record which can be shown to the General Medical Council if they request it, as to how attending a particular lecture or a course is going to change my practice. The costs to society and to doctors personally, of what are thankfully quite rare malpractice events, are enormous. We spend huge amounts of money on investigations to exclude the unlikely and the rare, just to avoid litigation – the number of x rays and scans undertaken has increased over the past few years, and yet 1 in 2000 patients will develop a malignancy from the exposure to radiation that these tests involve. Doubtless the pendulum will swing the other way in years to come when relatives of these patients bring law suits against us for ordering these cancer causing tests, when their loved ones succumb to a so called iatrogenic (i.e. doctor caused) malignancy. It's known that about 5% of any professional group require further training and help, but the mechanisms we use at the moment to identify such under-performing doctors, let alone find measures to help them, are frankly laughable. Current mechanisms include ponderously recording every hour of *education* I undertake, be it reading an article or attending a conference, but at no time does a fellow GP sit in with me to see how I run a clinic, or have a look at my records.

Patients consult me about any number of issues. The most common would come under the spectrum of mental health issues, of which anxiety and low mood makes up the majority. Next would be short term acute illnesses, such as viral infections, chest and ear, nose and throat infections. Musculoskeletal issues make up the next most common complaint. Increases in longevity mean that I have patients who are living with a number of long term conditions – they have had a heart attack or a stroke, or have lung disease such as asthma. Often we have diagnosed them as having risk factors which put them at increased chance of developing complications (such as heart attacks). Examples of these include high blood pressure and raised sugar levels (it is quite rare now for a patient to come and see us with new symptoms suggestive of diabetes). Many patients take a number of medications – it's not uncommon for them to take five to eight different medications a day, and it's a balancing act between benefits of these and side effects.

Of the consultations I enjoy the most are those where the patient comes to see me with depression. Teasing out the issues and working through them together is very satisfying. It's very sad though when someone comes with worrying symptoms and my suspicions are proved correct, when the cause of the problem is an inoperable cancer. I don't particularly enjoy consultations where I feel that the patient is resistant to suggestions for change leaving me wondering why they consulted me in the first place. I suspect that for a number of people being 'ill' is what they identify themselves as being and that being 'treated' is the last thing they want.

Diabetes itself is a disease which has increased dramatically in incidence since my grandmother's time. I expect she would have had one or two children who had it, but I suspect that the so called *'non-insulin-dependent diabetes'* which is strongly correlated with obesity was something she never saw. A significant number of my patients are overweight – over three-quarters of the population over the age of forty-five are, and obesity starts at an ever younger age. Lots of research is being devoted to why this might be, as it's not quite as simple as having an excess of calories (i.e. food intake being greater than energy output). Certainly the types of food we eat are very different now. A striking difference between my grandmother's time and now is that obesity is more commonly found in those of lower socio-economic group than in the higher. Food is much cheaper than it used to be, plus it is much more readily available. Social norms such as sitting down at the table for family meals is now observed by a minority of families, while eating outside or on public transport is publicly acceptable. Huge advances have been made in food preservation, but the price of this is that food is now available in processed forms which have had high quantities of fats, sugars and salt added to them. Processes involved in food production mean that families no longer need to prepare meals but can purchase them ready made, or easily obtain them from Take Away and fast food outlets. At the same time, the diet industry is valued at billions of pounds globally as people try and lose the weight they have gained, but very few of them manage to do so long term. The connection between obesity and several types of cancer is increasingly well understood, also making a number of conditions worse (such as blood pressure and osteoarthritis).

So to the similarities. Like Sabina, we provide palliative care, that is, the care of dying patients. As GPs we provide cradle to grave care. It is one of the most satisfying parts of my work to support patients through the diagnosis of a terminal illness and looking after them in their final days and hours. There are times when I am at someone's bedside, it's quiet, because there is no more to be said, equipment, such as a huge hospital bed, takes up the entire sitting room or dining room, and chairs have been brought in for visitors. The patient is comfortable with the aid of a syringe driver supplying a constant supply of morphine. This is when I think that I am one of so many GPs over the years who have done exactly the same thing under similar circumstances.

Her observations of 'Social Care' are just as valid today. When the NHS was formed I think it was hoped that all illness would be cured within a few years, and there would not be a need for an NHS. As a result, social care was never included in it, which means that while health care is free at point of use, social care is means tested. There are areas of glaring unfairness – for instance, if you are "lucky" enough to be dying of cancer, all your care will be paid for by the State (and the taxpayer). If, however, you have dementia and you need someone to remind you to make yourself something to drink, then you have to pay for that. This is something that many people are not aware of and it causes no end of difficulties as families (just like in Sabina's time) have to find ways of looking after their elderly parents while still working themselves. The cost of nursing homes is very high (around £1,000 per week). It has to be paid by the resident if he or she has any assets including a home worth more than £6,000 (I think). Politicians love to promise that nobody will have to sell their home to pay for care, but nevertheless the nursing home bill is settled as part of the estate instead.

I feel that Sabina is also with me in spirit rolling her eyes and muttering 'Oh, for heaven's sake' under her breath when I am dealing with patients who have panicked themselves into thinking they have cancer or some other serious illness, because they have read an article on Google and are not able to put it into context. Sabina seems, in common with GPs of present day, to have had little time for demanding patients, recognising perhaps that those who want it most may not necessarily need it the most.

I would love to show her and talk to her about medicine today. I wonder what she would say about our computer systems enabling me to find the information I need at the click of a button, or about antibiotics or other medicines which mean that so many conditions are not fatal any more. I would hope she would be pleased that we have made huge progress towards eliminating the sort of poverty that she describes, that we have more vaccinations (although I suspect her meeting an 'anti-vaxxer' i.e. someone who refuses to vaccinate their children against common childhood diseases, would leave her bewildered at their stupidity) and treatments for heart attacks, TB, and strokes which killed so many of her patients. I wonder what she would think when the leading cause of death of men and women under the age of forty five is suicide, and that it is dementia for the over seventies. It is interesting that she worked hard to try and alleviate some of the causes of ill health by arranging supplies of food and vitamins for children as an example, but I am not sure what she would say about how a nationalised health service is now expected to alleviate a significant number of societal woes which have their source in poor job prospects, low educational attainment and poverty.

I don't think she had a word for 'stress'. She talks about being exhausted and having three months off with heart trouble. She seems to have been taken by surprise by the attempted suicide of a patient. I'm struck by her compassion towards young couples finding themselves unexpectedly pregnant and needing help. There's little about organised religion in her diary at a time when the Church was very influential in society. I wonder if she was so determinedly scientific in her approach that there was little room for it. She also talks about finding pleasure in being given flowers or being able to enjoy the out-doors. She made the link between poverty and ill health years before the term 'inverse care law' became commonly used (which shows that those who need most care are the least likely to obtain it). This seems to have been a large part of her motivation to be a doctor.

Sabina wrote this diary five years before she died, killed during World War II for doing what she felt was the right and patriotic thing to do, and saving her sixteen year old son in the process. I wonder if she ever regretted working as a doctor – her frustrations with the system of payments and the difficulty reaching some of her patients comes over loud and clear, but I suspect she did not regret the choices she made. I don't think I would either.

I view practicing medicine to be a vocation and an immense privilege. I think my patients are aware of this as they show their appreciation and thanks at Christmas and at other times. I am also aware that this is not the experience of many patients who find that they cannot see the same GP twice, or that when they do, they find an overworked and harassed professional who I hope is doing the best he or she can under trying circumstances. I am very sorry for those patients and am also sorry for members of my profession who do not have the courage or self awareness to stop inflicting their frustrations onto their patients. Being in the Army taught me the term *'moral courage'* – doing the right thing, even when it is hard to do, is probably the best way to describe it. It is very difficult for me to work with people who do not possess this characteristic, because I think even if nothing else, we are paid quite well for doing what we do, and we, at the very least, should do our best in response to that.

I am writing this now during the time of an outbreak of a worldwide epidemic of a respiratory virus known as Covid 19. Epidemics on this scale are seen about once a century. This one has brought almost the whole world to an economic standstill as the only way to manage the rate of infection has been to advise whole populations to separate themselves from each other. Only time will tell if this is the right approach to take. Over a frighteningly short space of time our lives have been turned upside down as we stay at home, only leaving to go to buy food or work if we can't do so from home. As this virus seems to have a predilection for being increasingly fatal in the frail and elderly, we are suddenly talking about death more openly. We have now spent a year living with this epidemic. Vaccination against the infection is being rolled out to almost everyone (currently not to young children as it seems that they do not infect others).

As a practice, we have used a phone first appointment system for our patients for a number of years which means that we have spoken to our patients on the phone before seeing them as usually only a third to a half need seeing face to face. We have adapted our practice to try and ensure that anyone with suspected Covid 19 infection either doesn't come into the practice at all or is seen in a separate room which can then be decontaminated. As all UK GP practices have taken on this approach, there is no doubt that mistakes have been made along the way and a number of patients who should have been seen have not been. Also patients having been told that we are very busy trying to vaccinate or manage infected patients, have kept away. As a result we are now seeing a number of patients presenting late with their symptoms or when they finally do consult, they have a long list of questions which take much longer than before to sort out.

A year ago we thought that this epidemic would be over in just a few short weeks. How wrong we were. Governments around the world have printed money to keep their economies going, but paying off these loans will have long term implications for years to come. There has been a huge rise in mental health problems due to isolation. Studies are just being undertaken to show the impact on children's education the closing of schools has had. We have millions of patients now waiting for tests and operations which could not take place while hospitals in the UK were close to being overwhelmed by patients infected by Covid 19. We doctors worry how many patients have stayed at home, not wanting to bother us with their symptoms which might show more advanced cancers when we finally do see them. I suspect the long term effects will be with us for some time. I have over the years joined a number of organisations involved with longer term strategic planning. We hope to make a difference one day.

April 2021

Acknowledgements

This book would not have been written without my mother's help to me and her translation of Sabina's book. I have no idea how Sabina's book ever came to light – we have a copy dated Warsaw 1956 from a specialist medical publishing company. Sabina's photo survived by being hidden inside an oven during the bombardment of Warsaw – again, I don't know how my father was reunited with it given that his only possessions as he left Warsaw in 1943 were the clothes he stood up in, a brick from the rubble, a watch and a spoon. My thanks also go to Stefan Cembrowicz for his support with editing and by writing the foreword. Also I must thank Paul and Lois Goddard for helping me with the publication.

Last but by no means least, my husband Alan, my children Alex and Abby and, of course, all my patients.

Dr. Monika Blackwell